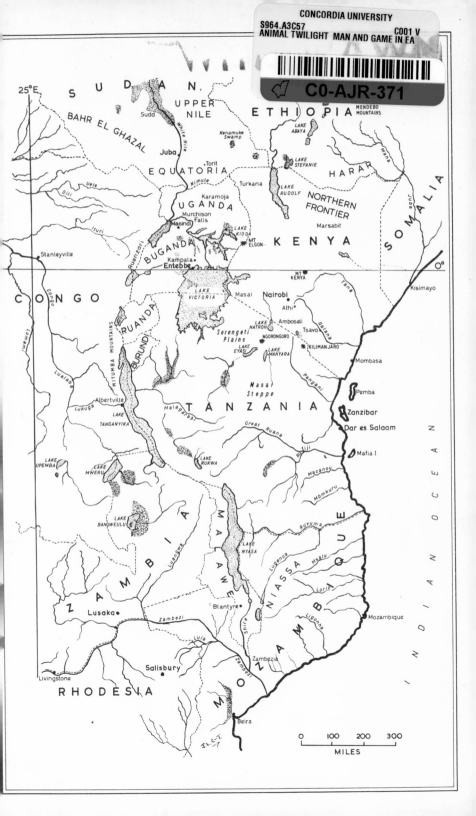

25°E.

S U D A N.   N.
UPPER
BAHR EL GHAZAL   NILE   ETHIOPIA   MENDEBO
                                              MOUNTAINS
Sudd
White Nile
LAKE
ABAYA
Juba
Kenamuke
Swamp
Torit
EQUATORIA   Turkana   LAKE
                               STEFANIE   HARAR
Nimule
LAKE
RUDOLF   NORTHERN
Karamoja   FRONTIER
UGANDA
Uele
Dili
Ituri
Murchison   Marsabit
Masindi   Falls
BUGANDA   LAKE   MT   KENYA
               KIOGA   ELGON
Stanleyville   Ruwenzori   Kampala
                                     Entebbe   Kisimayo
                              MT
                              KENYA   0°
CONGO   LAKE
             VICTORIA   Masai   Nairobi
RUANDA   Athi   Tana
BURUNDI   Serengeti   LAKE   Amboseli   Tsavo
               Plains   NATRON   Galana
                            LAKE   NGORONGORO   KILIMANJARO
Lualaba   LAKE   EYASI   LAKE
               NATRON   MANYARA   Mombasa
Albertville   MITUMBA MOUNTAINS
Lukuga   LAKE   Malagarasi   Masai   Pemba
              TANGANYIKA   Steppe   Pangani
                        TANZANIA   Zanzibar
LAKE   Great Ruaha   Dar es Salaam
UPEMBA   LAKE
              MWERU   LAKE   Rufiji   Mafia I
                         RUKWA
LAKE   Macanoy
BANGWEULU   Mbmkuru

Luangwa   M   Ruvuma
Luapula   A   LAKE   Lugenoa
               L   NYASA   Msalu   NIASSA
Z   A
A   M   W   Lugenoa
M   B   E   Lurio
B   I   MOZAMBIQUE
I   A   Blantyre
     Lusaka   Zambezi   Shire   Ligonna   Mozambique
                            Luia
     Salisbury   Zambezia
Livingstone   Zambezi

RHODESIA   M
                O
                Z
                A
                M
                B
                I
                Q
                U
                E   Beira

J.L.C.T.

0   100   200   300
MILES

INDIAN OCEAN

SOMALIA
Juba

Animal
Twilight

Books by the same Author:

BIOLOGY OF DESERTS (*Ed.*)

SPIDERS, SCORPIONS, CENTIPEDES AND MITES

ANIMAL BEHAVIOUR

LAND INVERTEBRATES (*with John Sankey*)

RHYTHMIC ACTIVITY IN ANIMAL PHYSIOLOGY AND BEHAVIOUR

LIFE IN DESERTS (*with M. J. Chadwick*)

DESERT LIFE

ANIMAL CONFLICT AND ADAPTATION

MICROECOLOGY

ANIMAL TWILIGHT

Man and Game in Eastern Africa

J. L. CLOUDSLEY-THOMPSON

DUFOUR

1967

*First published in Great Britain
by G. T. Foulis & Co Ltd 1967*

Dufour Editions, Inc.
Chester Springs
Pennsylvania

Library of Congress Catalog Card Number 67/20889

Printed in Great Britain by The Whitefriars Press Limited
London & Tonbridge

91175

CONTENTS

▼

ILLUSTRATIONS

HISTORICAL DRAWINGS

ACKNOWLEDGMENTS

In preparing this account, nearly two thousand books have been consulted, of which less than ten per cent are listed in the Bibliography. No doubt there are many more that I ought to have looked at: even so, selection of material for quotation has not always been easy. In general, where the same thing has been described by a number of authors, I have tried to choose the more vivid accounts. Hunting yarns and tales of exploration have seldom been of value for my purpose, unless they gave unbiased accounts of wild life as it was in the past, before the advent of the European. Occasionally I have quoted from such books—when they shed light on aspects of animal behaviour or provide graphic illustrations of Africa, years ago. In the comprehensive term eastern Africa I have included that part of the continent lying roughly south of the Sahara and east of about longitude 25°E. I have not dealt with West Africa although occasional references have been made to some of the tribes from that region, especially the Fan. I am greatly indebted to the publishers of the various books listed for permission to make quotations and reproduce figures. My thanks are also due to zoological colleagues who have been kind enough to send me their publications. Again, though only a selection of references is given in the text, my ideas have been influenced by reading many other articles that I have not actually cited. I should also like to express my gratitude to Prof. A. J. Whiteman for his comments on Chapter 1, to Mrs. Elizabeth Khalil for typing the manuscript, and to Mr. John Hassell for his most helpful criticism and advice. Finally, I am deeply grateful to Dr. Hugh B. Cott Sc.D., D.Sc., F.R.P.S. for his generosity in providing a selection of his magnificent photographs of African game.

J. L. C-T.

Khartoum
March 1966

'Thorkild had given back before his Devil, till the bowmen in the ship could shoot it all full of arrows.' (An out-dated conception of animal ferocity.) From Rudyard Kipling (1908). *Puck of Pook's Hill.* London: Macmillan.

Chapter I

THE IMPACT OF MAN

Recent discoveries have shown unequivocally that much of human evolution has taken place in the continent of Africa. When man first emerged as a tool-maker, some two million years ago, the African fauna was much richer than it is today. At least 58 large Bovidae and some 20 species of pigs are known to have existed then. Since that time, however, many species of plants and animals have been exterminated by climatic changes, failure of adaptation and, possibly, by poisonous gases, flame, fire and ashes from volcanoes. Only a small proportion of the original fauna has actually died out as a result of human activities.

A modern illustration of the effects of volcanic action is afforded by the volcano Oldoinyo Lengai. In and around its crater are greyish white patches of ash coated with sodium carbonate. Although this is regularly leached out by the rains, it is renewed at intervals from small vents and fissures. In 1917, 1954 and 1960, eruptions occurred which shrouded the surrounding countryside with soda-permeated ash. When the rains fell, water holes became fouled with bitter salts and many herds of cattle and wild game died through drinking from the contaminated pools.

In the early stages of his existence, man was compelled to live near water as he had no means of carrying and storing it. At first he had no weapons either, only simple cutting tools, and lived on insects, molluscs, frogs, fishes, reptiles and small mammals, supplemented by coarse vegetable matter and occasional scavenging from the prey of the larger carnivores. The invention of weapons for hunting extended his food supply, but not his range from water.

Thus, as Dr. L. S. B. Leakey (1951) has shown, the early Australopithecine men of the Olduvai Gorge, near the Ngorongoro crater made pebble tools—stones with one end chipped into cutting edges. They subsisted by food-gathering, and hunted baboons, gazelles and other small game, tortoises, rodents, bats and birds, the bones of which have been found along with their own.

When he had learned to store water in ostrich egg shells, skins and baskets lined with clay, man was able to live further from streams and pools. Then, with the invention of fire, he was able to inhabit colder places too and to smoke out the wild bees in order to gather honey. Only in the later agricultural stages of development was fire used deliberately to destroy the forest, but it may have been used before this to kill or panic herds of game in hunting.

Early man in eastern Africa was able to exploit a wide range of altitudes from sea-level to about 6,000 ft., so that climatic changes did not affect him adversely, as they did in Europe and Asia where he was driven away by the advance of the ice. Moreover, there was an abundance of animal life for food so that conditions were generally favourable. With the development of stone knives and cutting tools, man was able to build crude huts, to follow the migration routes of game animals and, eventually, to compete as a hunter with the larger carnivores. The rhinoceros and elephant were favourite subjects of Upper Palaeolithic art. They were caught in traps and probably figured on the menus of the cave kitchens of those times.

In the words of Sir Harry Johnston, writing about 1910: 'During the Pliocene[1] and Pleistocene periods . . . Mediterranean Africa had developed or had received from Europe and Asia the magnificent fauna which makes the tropical regions of this continent the world's great wonderland in Natural History at the present day. Various causes—the cold breath of the Ice Ages, the attacks of Neolithic Man, the increased drought, and lack of water and vegetation—drove this medley of beasts out of Mauretania, Egypt and Libya into the recesses of tropical Africa where they remain; giraffes and okapis; buffaloes, elands and bush bucks; antelope innumerable, wart hogs, forest pigs and bush pigs; hippopotami; rhinoceroses, zebras and asses; elephants and hyraxes; the manis and ant-bear edentates; lions, leopards, cheetahs and lynxes; hyaenas, jackals and hunting dogs; monkeys, baboons, and great apes'.

There is no doubt that, of the factors he mentioned, water-shortage was the most important in reducing the fauna. Even today, accessibility to water dominates the tropical African scene. Many areas of pasture land do not carry their full weight of game animals simply because of water shortage whilst, in the pluvial conditions of the Pleistocene there were not only many more species, but giant sheep and buffaloes, and pigs as large as rhinos.

During the last glaciation, for at least 50,000 years prior to 15,000 B.C., the temperature of Africa must have averaged about 5 deg. C. lower than at present. The corresponding reduction in evaporation would have increased the effectiveness of the rainfall so

---

[1]The Pliocene epoch lasted from 12-15 million years to about one million years B.C.; the Pleistocene then followed, lasting until about 11,000 years B.C. J. L. C.-T.

that forest animals, which are at present reduced to small, isolated montane areas, spread right across Africa from the west.[2]

The Great Rift Valley is an open area of grassland, probably produced as a result of innumerable fires caused by volcanic action, through which animals and man have migrated freely since Pleistocene times. In the Middle Pleistocene there were many little volcanoes between Kilimanjaro and Mount Kenya, each of which was capable of starting fires that might range from 50 to 60 miles or more. As we shall see, fire is one of the most important features in producing grassland savannah.

Stone-age men were primarily hunters and fishermen. The transition to agriculture and stock breeding that made possible the development of settlements and villages spread but slowly down the Nile Valley. Although palaeolithic hunters must have been an important element in African ecology, they could have had little effect on the distribution of mammals because they did not influence the environment. With the development of pastoralism and agriculture, however, the habitat was changed and this affected the fauna very greatly.

According to Hediger (1955), apart from the donkey, only the cat and the guinea-fowl have been domesticated in Africa. Indeed, the failure of African peoples to assume any relationship with wild animals, other than that of hunting them, is surprising considering the abundance of zebras, antelopes, buffaloes and so on. Except for the Balala of the Kalahari, who are said formerly to have tamed wild dogs and taught them to hunt, only the ancient Egyptians were keepers and breeders of animals: they partially domesticated some birds and antelopes but, later, their attempts at breeding disappeared. Even the breeding of the Watussi cattle of Inyambo for ritual purposes did not originate in the Congo or Ruanda, but has come down with many modifications from ancient Egypt. In the Congo, where, even today, 10,000—20,000 elephants are killed annually, no experiments were made of taming them until, in 1880, the missionaries of Saint Anne-de-Fernand Vaz in the Gabon succeeded in doing so and people came from miles around to see the miracle![3]

In the same vein, Sir Samuel Baker (1890) wrote: 'There is no reason why the African elephants should not be tamed and made useful, but the difficulty lies in obtaining them in any great numbers. The natives of Africa are particularly savage, and their instincts of destruction prevent them from capturing and domesticating any wild animals. During nine years' experience of Central Africa I never saw a tamed creature of any kind, not even a bird or a young antelope in possession of a child. . . . So few African elephants have been tamed

[2]Moreau, R. E. (1963), *Proc. Zool. Soc. London.* **141**, 395-421.
[3]See page 144.

in proportion to those of Asia that it would be difficult to pronounce an opinion upon their character when domesticated, but it is generally believed by their trainers that the Indian species is more gentle and amenable to discipline'.

On the other hand, Dr. David Livingstone wrote in his journal for 12 July 1872: 'The ancient Africans seem to have been at least as early as the Asiatics in the art of taming elephants. The Egyptian monuments show them bringing tame elephants and lions into Egypt; and very ancient sculptures show the real African species, which the artist must have seen. They refused to sell elephants, which cost them months of hard labour to catch and tame, to a Greek commander of Egyptian troops for a few brass pots: they were quite right. Two or three tons of fine fat butcher-meat were far better than the price, seeing their wives could make any number of cooking pots for nothing'.

It is unwise to generalise about a continent as large as Africa: until a couple of thousand years ago, forest elephants, *Loxodonta africana cyclotis*, were widespread from the Mediterranean to the Cape (p. 141). As we shall see, only this subspecies is capable of domestication: the larger bush elephant, *L. africana africana*, becomes quite unmanageable when adult. It is the bush elephant which inhabits the savannah of eastern Africa and bears the largest tusks.

The use of fire for cooking and the invention of clay pots, which must greatly have reduced the amount of parasitism and disease resulting from eating raw meat, probably initiated an increase in population numbers which was accelerated by the development of agriculture.[4]

Nevertheless, game was fairly plentiful in many places. Most game animals are sufficiently fecund to tolerate a reasonable degree of cropping by human as well as animal predators. Indeed, there was probably a kind of symbiosis between the game animals and the indigenous population.

In order to cultivate the soil in tropical regions patches of land are cleared of vegetation, trees are felled above ground level and burned, leaving the ground bristling with decapitated trunks but rich with fertile ashes. For a few years good crops are obtained but, when all the salts have been leached by rain from the soil, the shifting cultivator moves to another virgin area and repeats his process of destruction.

Over the centuries, the forests of eastern Africa have thus been replaced by savannah. The term 'savannah' comes from an American Indian word for natural grasslands in northern tropical America.

[4]Cowles, R. B. (1963). *Amer. Midl. Nat.* **97**, 29-37.

These grasslands are floristically and edaphically[5] very similar but form an ecological unit which differs materially from the grasslands of tropical Africa. There is no characteristic savannah climate, but a characteristic association of soil and land form. The tropical savannah ecosystem is not a climax, but is maintained largely by the delicately balanced interaction of climate, soils, vegetation, animals and fire. The association between animal and plant life is extremely complex and alteration of any of the components of the dynamic equilibrium usually alters the whole ecosystem—that is, the ecological system formed by the interaction of all the animals and plants with their environment. Although frequent fires occur, they are not always necessary for the maintenance of savannah.[6]

In East Africa, however, savannah has long been maintained by regular burning of the grass. Without this, the conditions which used to support such magnificent herds of wild beasts and, in parts, still do so, would never have been created. It has been noticed in national parks that the protection of a portion of the savannah encourages the growth of trees and causes a retreat of the grass, owing to the stopping of fires. In this way, the environment becomes less favourable to the big ruminants and their carnivorous followers and the fauna changes. Thus, the pastoral people who for centuries have regularly burned the grass to provide grazing for their cattle, have been responsible for the evolution of vast herds of game animals which could be hunted with primitive weapons without any threat to their survival. But, with the advent of fire-arms and recent increase in human population, the whole situation has changed.

The oldest cereal crops in Africa south of the Sahara were millets of various kinds and rice in West Africa. (Bananas and yams have been introduced from Asia whilst maize and cassava, the most important food crops of today, came from America during the 16th and 17th centuries A.D.)

Six or seven thousand years ago, at the dawn of agriculture, there were four main human racial types living in Africa: the Caucasian Hamites who were migrating down the Nile valley from the north, the Bushmen, Pigmies and Negroes. The Pigmies had probably evolved in the forests of the Congo and the Bushmen in the more open country to the east and south. The origin of the Negroes is uncertain, but the evidence suggests that they first appeared as fishermen to the north of the equatorial forest at a time when the southern Sahara received more rain than it does today.[7]

Africa has little in the way of recorded history except, of course, for

[5]Edaphically—influenced by conditions of the soil or substratum.
[6]Beard, J. S. (1953). *Ecol. Monogr.* **23**, 149-215.
[7]Fage & Oliver, 1962.

Egypt, before the coming of Europeans. The first Europeans to establish themselves in eastern Africa were the Portuguese. In 1487 Bartolomew Diaz succeeded in passing the Cape of Good Hope and sighted Algoa Bay where Port Elizabeth now stands. A few years later, his countryman Vasco da Gama proceeded further and reached Natal. Soon afterwards, the Arab trading settlements on the eastern coast of Africa fell to the Portuguese, but they did not attempt to establish a depot where Cape Town now stands to connect their West and East African spheres of commerce. About 1650, they were ejected from many of their possessions by the Arabs of Oman and have retained only Mozambique until present times.

The history of South and East Africa really dates from 1652 when the Dutch East India Company founded a settlement at the Cape, where their merchant ships could be re-victualled on voyages to and from the east. At first, immigrants were encouraged in order to provide defence of the settlement and an adequate supply of food for passing East Indiamen. But soon the colonists began to chafe against restrictions and eventually began a series of treks eastwards towards Natal.

Now for many years the Bantu tribes from the north had been extending their territory in the fertile coastal plains between the Drakensberg mountains and the sea, driving Hottentot and Bushmen before them whenever they required more land. It is believed that the Hottentots were created by Hamitic people inter-marrying with Bushmen, for the Caucasian Hamites, who were cultivators and pasturalists, extended deep into southern Africa as recently as one thousand years ago.[8]

The Bushmen originally inhabited a vast area of eastern Africa stretching from the Red Sea coast to South West Africa. The Moslem chronicler, Massoudi of Baghdad, wrote in *The Golden Meadows* (A.D. 915) of the little Wak-wak people, identified as Bushmen, in the region of Sofala whilst Idrisi in his map of 1154 showed them as inhabiting this part of south-east Africa.[9] As late as the middle 19th century, the Bushmen were dispersed over a much greater area of southern Africa than at present and official records show that the Dutch settlers first encountered them 50 miles to the north of the Cape settlement in April 1655. At first known as Sonquas, they came, some time later, to be called Bosjesmen.

The Bushmen were extremely skilled and cunning hunters, using snares and pit-traps. They were magnificent archers and could hit a moving buck with a poisoned arrow at a range of 150 yards. So confident were they that one man would annoy a bull elephant or rhino until it charged, when a companion would run up and ham-

[8]Fage & Oliver, 1962.
[9]P. V. Tobias pp. 67-86 *in* Davis, D. H. S., 1964.

string it so that it could easily be finished off with knives and spears. At times, the Bushmen would frighten game in the direction of a hungry lion. They would let the lion kill and eat enough to still its hunger and then drive it off with smoke and fire in order to obtain the rest of the meat. J. Campbell wrote in 1815 that the chief amusements of their children were shooting arrows at insects and beasts, and throwing assegais. He added: 'These people are far from possessing nice stomachs, for they can eat, with relish, the flesh of elephants, lions, tigers, camel-leopards, quackas &c. Yesterday I observed one of them kill a goat by thrusting into its belly a long awl, which appeared a cruel operation, but it is their method'.

A. Sparrman (1785) gave further details of the Bushman's diet: 'Their table, however, is sometimes composed of several other dishes, among which may be reckoned the larvae of insects, or those of caterpillars from which butterflies are generated; and in like manner a sort of white ants (the *termes*), grasshoppers, snakes and some sorts of spiders. With all these changes of diet, the Boshies-man is nevertheless frequently in want, and famished to such a degree, as to waste almost to a shadow'.

According to Sir Harry Johnston (1910): 'The earliest type of Bushman in South Africa seems to have been the "Strand-loopers", (Shore-runners) of the Dutch, the remains of whom are found in caves along the Natal coast. There is also alleged to be another dwarfish race still existing in South Africa at the present day—the "Vaalpens" of the Boers, but called "Katea", "Ikoei", "Kosobala" by the Bechuanas and Zulus. They were first described by the French traveller, M. Belegorgue[10], in 1847. They are said to have a much darker skin than the Bushmen, and to live in an even lower state of culture, to be cannibals (which the Bushmen are not), and to have more abundant head-hair. The men also have thick beards (the beard is usually absent in the Bushmen). According to Belegorgue they scarcely reached to 4 ft. in height, and they generally lived in holes and hollows carved out of huge anthills. Truly about the lowest recorded type of *Homo sapiens*'.

For all their skill, the Bushmen could not withstand the onslaught of the Bantu and, caught in a vast nut-cracker between them and the Boers, were either exterminated or forced westwards into the inhospitable wastes of the Kalahari desert where the remnants of their descendants still manage to survive.

Firmly convinced that they were the elect of God and that no heathen coloured races had any rights to the land, the Boers dispersed the Hottentots and pushed eastwards, hunting down the Bushmen until, towards the end of the eighteenth century, they ran against

[10]*Voyage dans l'Afrique Australe.* Vol. 2, pp. 548-9.

the strongly organised Bantu tribes and there began a series of Kaffir wars which persisted for the next hundred years.

The first result of the clash between the Boers and the Bantu was that the latter could no longer enlarge their territory except at the expense of their neighbours. On the death of Dingiswayo, in 1818, Chaka murdered all his heirs and became king of the Zulus. In 1809, Dr. Cowan had been sent by Lord Caledon, Governor of the Cape, to seek an overland trade route to Delgoa Bay. During a stay of six months in Dingiswayo's kraal, it is said that he told Chaka that the British army conquered by the use of the bayonet. At any rate, on his accession, Chaka abolished the long and not particularly effective throwing spear that was the traditional weapon of his people and taught his well-disciplined impis to discard their sandals and fight at close quarters with the *Iklwa*, a single broad-bladed stabbing spear. Until the development of effective long range weapons like guns and the bows of British archers in the Middle Ages, people, such as the Zulus and Romans who were prepared to fight, maintain discipline, and kill at close quarters, were usually victorious.

Spear-throwing tribes could not stand against Chaka's impis wielding the new weapon he had devised. When he had enlisted 60,000 men, Chaka raided eastern Cape Colony on the plateau which later became the Transvaal and Orange Free State. During his career he killed over three million people and conquered a territory larger than Europe within a period of 12 years. In 1826 he, himself, was murdered by his brothers Dingaan and Mahlangaga. His corpse was wrapped in a green ox hide and thrown into a corn pit.

Dingaan, who succeeded him, was scarcely less cruel yet lacked Chaka's courage and personality. He attacked the Boer pioneers who, from 1836, began to cross the Drakensberg into Natal. He lured their leader and 60 men into his kraal at Umgunghlovu, massacred them and then killed hundreds of women and children. He was defeated, however, in 1838 by 800 Boers who burnt his capital. He fled north and was murdered on the Pangola river by N'Gawo. He was followed by Panda, Cetewayo, Dinizulu and Solomon.

The effects of the Zulu outburst were felt throughout southern Africa. Some tribes copied the Zulus and themselves set out on careers of conquest: the Makololo conquered the Barotse kingdom on the upper Zambesi and another group marched westwards into Bechuanaland. In Swaziland and Basutoland the refugees merged together and became sufficiently strong to withstand the Zulus. At the same time, some of the Zulu formations struck out on careers of conquest of their own. After their leaders had quarrelled with Chaka, the warriors of

[11]Fage & Oliver, 1962.

Zwangendaba eventually settled as far away as the shores of Lake Nyasa.[11] The Matabele Empire was founded by the Zulu warrior Mzilikazi who, in his rise to power, exterminated 28 tribes and ravaged half a million square miles of Africa.

Laurens van der Post (1958) relates that his grandfather remembered his father telling him that when the Boers first felt their way into the country across the Great River (the Orange River), they found that all the lions were man-eaters. The many thousands of dead bodies left on the veld after a generation of massacre and counter-massacre by Korannas, Griquas, Mantatus, Zulu, Matabele and Barolong, had given the lions such a taste for human flesh that they ignored game whenever it was possible to hunt human prey.

Turning now to the middle of East Africa, apart from the coastal regions, little was known of tropical East Africa until the advent of explorers such as J. H. Speke, Sir Francis Burton, Sir Samuel Baker, Dr. David Livingstone and Sir Henry Stanley. This late development was undoubtedly due largely to the prevalence of disease and especially of malaria in this region. At first a source of slaves, which were sent either to Zanzibar or down the Nile into Egypt, East Africa later became even more important for its ivory. The hunting of elephant on a vast scale required arms and ammunition, which could also be used in warfare, whilst slaves were still required as porters to transport the tusks to the coast. Consequently slavery and its attendant evils were almost inseparable from the ivory trade and continued for a long while despite many years of British diplomatic and naval effort.

It was the possession of European-manufactured firearms which gave slave and ivory traders, both from Egypt and from Zanzibar, the confidence to invade long-established native civilisations and enabled them to succeed in competition with all other traders. At the same time, the introduction of guns again spelt destruction to the game animals of yet another region of the African continent.

To the forefront of the Colonists, both in South and East Africa, were the hunters who provided them with meat, usually dried to form biltong. These hunters often made fortunes from the ivory, rhinoceros horn and the other animal by-products they obtained in their dangerous and exciting lives. Probably few of them realised that the vast herds they encountered could ever be endangered by their activities. To a certain extent, of course, they were right. Market hunting alone will seldom exterminate a species because it is only economic in regions where animals are abundant. When they become scarce, the hunter must move on to new grounds, leaving the survivors to breed up again. The trouble is that these survivors were not left alone: stockbreeders and farmers can always spare the time to shoot off the odd elephant or rhino on their land, and when animals become scarce the snares and poisoned arrows of the African have an enhanced effect.

As a result of all this slaughter, game animals tend to be rare, or non-existent in most of Africa except in national parks and game reserves and, even here, their continued existence is in danger.

In this chapter I have tried to indicate that climatic and other natural changes have been primarily responsible for the decimation of wild animals in Africa since Pleistocene times. Human beings were not originally harmful; indeed their activities in degrading rainforest to savannah were largely responsible for the production of vast herds of big ruminants and their carnivorous predators. It is only comparatively recently, with the advent of fire-arms and the human population explosion, that the wild-life of eastern Africa has been endangered by man.

Elephant—battue among the Fans. From P. B. du Chaillu (1861).

CHAPTER II

TRADITIONAL AFRICAN HUNTING METHODS

FROM time immemorial, the balance of nature, in so far as elephant are concerned, has been maintained by man, the toll of calves taken by carnivores being slight.[1] The same is probably true of most if not all other big game. In this chapter, I shall review the various methods traditionally used by African natives for killing big game. Almost without exception, these are wasteful, inefficient and cruel: they are now illegal everywhere. Nevertheless, on account of their inefficiency, they could seldom actually endanger game populations unless operating in conjunction with other factors.

By no means all African people are good hunters, a fact mentioned by many earlier explorers in accounts of their travels. For example, Captain F. S. Quicke, during his travels in East Africa towards the end of the last century was struck with the uselessness of the people of one region in the art. Game was plentiful, but they appeared totally ignorant of their habits and unable to spoor except where the tracks were most definitely apparent. Like other animals, man is very conservative. People seldom voluntarily change their ways of life. Some tribes live by hunting because they have always done so. Others are agriculturalists or, like the Masai and Karamojong, live on the blood of their cattle. Although wild game may be plentiful, they do not hunt. Only when food has become really scarce will a hunting tribe change its mode of existence, and the natural resistance of nomadic peoples to settlement is a constant problem to governments of arid countries like Sudan.

Many African tribes were, and are, extremely courageous, as will appear from the accounts given in the following pages. Naturally, however, there are exceptions. Major W. Cornwallis Harris, for instance, had no high opinion of Ethiopian courage in elephant hunting. He wrote in his *Highlands of AEthiopia* (1844): 'On the first intimation of the animals having, after two days' diligent search, been actually discovered, three fourths of the whole party had incontinently disappeared. The Galla horsemen, who had previously boasted the destruction of elephants with their spears, did not venture to approach for a full hour after their ears had been saluted by the

[1]Blunt, 1933.

11

reports of the rifles; and even the warrior who vaunted himself the "hereditary chieftain of all the Braves of the Amhara nation", long clung pertinaciously to his secure seat amongst the topmost branches.' William Astor Chanler (1896), writing of Kenya, gives another example: 'The country was literally alive with elephants; but these natives, fearing to spear them, trusted entirely in their traps, which the sagacity of the elephant frequently enabled him to avoid'.

Fire

Stone-age men probably developed a number of methods for killing game, using devices that are still employed today among primitive tribes. One of the earliest of these was to ring a herd with fire and burn the animals to death. The technique has been described by Sir Samuel Baker (1890) as follows: 'During the dry season, when the withered herbage from 10 to 14 feet in height is most inflammable, a large herd of elephants may be found in the middle of such high grass that they can only be perceived should a person be looking down from some elevated point. If they should be espied by some native hunter, he would immediately give due notice to the neighbourhood, and in a short time the whole population would assemble for the hunt. This would be arranged by forming a circle of perhaps 2 miles in diameter, and simultaneously firing the grass so as to create a ring of flames around the centre. An elephant is naturally afraid of fire, and it has an instinctive horror of the crackling of flames when the grass has been ignited. As the circle of fire contracts in approaching the encircled herd, they at first attempt retreat until they become assured of their hopeless position; they at length become desperate, being maddened by fear, and panic-stricken by the wild shouts of the thousands who have surrounded them. At length, half suffocated by the dense smoke, and terrified by the close approach of the roaring flames, the unfortunate animals charge recklessly through the fire, burnt and blinded, to be ruthlessly speared by the bloodthirsty crowd awaiting this last stampede. Sometimes a hundred or more elephants are simultaneously destroyed in this wholesale slaughter. The flesh is then cut into long strips and dried, every portion of the animal being smoked upon frames of green wood, and the harvest of meat is divided among the villages which have contributed to the hunt. The tusks are also shared, a certain portion belonging by right to the various headmen and the chief'.

At least until the second decade of the present century, the technique of hunting by fire was responsible for the death of many hundreds of elephants and other animals each year.[2]

[2]Carrington, 1958.

In his book, *The Heart of Africa* (1873) Dr. George Schweinfurth gave a similar account of hunting by the Niam-Niam (now called Azande) tribe of the southern Sudan. As soon as a force of people had been collected, the elephants were driven towards some tracts of dense grass that had been purposely spared from the steppe burning. Provided with firebrands, the crowd then surrounded the spot. The conflagration soon extended on all sides, until the poor brutes, choked and scorched, fell a helpless prey to their destroyers, who despatched them with their lances. Not only the males, with their large and valuable tusks, but the females also with the young, were, of course, included in this wholesale and indiscriminate slaughter, and Schweinfurth feared that this might result in extermination.

No doubt the hunting of elephants by fire greatly increased as a result of the European demand for ivory, but it was clearly a traditional method and the following description given by G. Casati (1891) shows that considerable organisation was required: 'The Abarambo are brave hunters of elephants, and the Mege alone surpass them in skill. They devote themselves to hunting of different kinds, according to the time of year, and the amount of preparation required. When the time arrives for the grass to be burnt, the company of hunters assemble, and the chief arranges each person's part in the operation, of which the principal are driving the animals together, killing them, and burning the grass. The men charged with driving, occupy a large zone of ground, and by beating drums put the animals in motion, managing to drive them into a pre-arranged spot, which ought to be grassy, where men appointed for the work assembled in a good number, set fire to all the surroundings. The elephants, terrified by the flames, rush into precipitate flight; they butt the fire, and becoming furious, dash at all points, when the greater part, blinded by the smoke and overtaken by the flames, fall and die in a short time. The few which succeed in reaching the only and narrow way left open, rush there as to a place of safety, but they fall into the traps prepared by the hunters, who kill them with lance thrusts'.

Although fire hunts were directed chiefly against elephant in order to produce both ivory and food, some tribes used the same technique to kill smaller animals for the pot. An example is provided by the Acholi of Uganda—Albert Lloyd (1906) described their method of hunting as follows: 'At this camp I saw for the first time the cruel practice of burning out the antelope and other animals, thus slaughtering male and female, old and young alike. When the jungle is dried up with the great heat of the dry season, a patch of country is chosen by the people as a likely one to contain species of fauna and the whole village population surround the spot—men, women and children taking part. Then at many places the grass is ignited, until a fierce fire barrier is made, effectually enclosing any animals that may be in it, and rendering escape impossible, for even should the poor frightened beast break through the flames, a solid phalanx of armed Acholi is beyond, ready to deal destruction with unerring aim with their spears. Here a small herd of kongoni were entrapped and several were killed, one or two escaping, owing to a break in the ranks of the hunters, but these got away frightfully burned, some to die a lingering death elsewhere'.

In the vast plains of the Congo, several villages used to unite for hunting in the season. They would fire the grass to windward of a district in which game abounded, in such a way as to make a vast circle of flame. The hunters then took their stand to leeward, holding long, stout nets, very like seines, or else armed with all sorts of sticks, stones and other missiles with which to kill the animals as they emerged, maddened by the smoke and the crackling of the fire.[3]

When the grass burned, great precautions were taken and a space cleared round each village. 'It is then that the natives kill the elephants to get the ivory. This indiscriminate slaughter of these animals will never last, though they seem plentiful enough from their marks in the wilderness near here. Ivory, except for certain instruments, is a mere luxury, and the cost of animal life to obtain it is not commensurate with its value'—so wrote General (then Colonel) Charles Gordon (1881) in his journal for 22 October 1875 when he was at Duffli near where the Sudan-Uganda border lies today. But again, he did not seem to realise that the method could only have been effective where game was plentiful, and therefore could not permanently endanger animal populations.

W. D. M. Bell (1960), the famous elephant hunter, gives a horrifying account of a fire hunt in French Equatorial Africa. 'Soon the fire trap became quite small. Now was when the fun should start in earnest. It was unbelievable the speed it went. On the trodden grass of the game trails the fire ran along at express speed. The major trouble was the poor visibility owing to smoke. You simply could not see what was going on. This was a pity because plenty was happening. As the fire contracted, so did the noise expand. There were now masses of infuriated natives dashing in and out of visibility on all sides. Some unrecognisable beast would burst through the throng with a milling mass of people apparently hanging on to it, spears jabbing everything going at it until it fell. Then a large bull elephant badly burnt and deeply dejected appeared with drooping ears and blisters the size of tea trays—a horrible sight. I quickly despatched him and examined his eyes. They were both scorched white to the eyeball. He could not have seen at all . . . And so it went all that awful day, far into the

[3]Cureau, 1911.

A sketch illustrating one method by which the African native attempts
to kill an elephant. From J. Bland-Sutton (1911).

night, a ghastly job. You could not leave those fire blitzed animals to the fumbling native equipment. I never knew how many buffalo and elephant I despatched that day. . . .'.

Similar accounts have been given by other travellers, but I think I have quoted enough to establish the contention that this method of hunting was wasteful and inefficient as well as revoltingly cruel. Nevertheless it was intermittent, and certainly far less lethal than the relentless slaughter by means of fire-arms, in the hands of both Africans and Europeans, that has taken place during the last two centuries.

Weighted spears

In many parts of equatorial Africa elephants were, and are occasionally even today, killed with weighted spears. These consist of a heavy block of wood, to one end of which is attached a sharp metal harpoon. A rope of lianas is attached to the block, its loose end passing over a horizontal bough. The block is raised to a height of about 18 to 20 ft. and the loose end of rope attached to a wooden bar supported across a game track. The height of the bar is such that small animals are able to pass beneath it, but bigger creatures such as elephants have to knock it aside. When this occurs, the heavy block falls, if all goes well, driving the metal harpoon deeply into the elephant's neck.

David Livingstone described such weighted spears in his journal for 3 January 1870: 'We passed several huge traps for elephants: they are constructed thus—a log of heavy wood, about 20 feet long, has a hole at one end for a climbing plant to pass through and suspend it, at the lower end a mortice is cut out of the side, and a wooden lance about 2 inches broad by 1½ thick, and about 4 feet long, is inserted firmly in the mortice; a latch down on the ground, when touched with the animal's foot, lets the beam run down on to his body, and the great weight of the wood drives in the lance and kills the animal. I saw one lance which had accidentally fallen, and it had gone into the stiff clay soil two feet'.

W. D. M. Bell (1923) mentions a falling spear with a 12 ft. shaft that weighed no less than 400 lbs. A rope of vine or creeper was stretched across an elephant path so that, in passing, the animal must snap it, thus liberating the spear to drop on its head or ribs.

These elephant spears are certainly formidable weapons. H. M. Stanley (1890) referred to one found on 8 April 1888, during his second journey from Fort Bodo to the Albert Nyanza. Shortly after leaving the Ituri river, he passed a place where an elephant spear had fallen to the ground, and buried itself so deep that three men were unable to heave it out. Such a force, he argued, would have slain an elephant on the instant.

A guillotine, invented by the Momfus for killing elephants, involved the same principle. The iron part consisted of a sickle about a span broad, with convex edge, and two blades diverging upwards. Between the blades was inserted a shaft of the same width, cut flat and weighted with a block of wood. The weight, in falling, drove the cutting part, shaft and all, deep into the elephant's back.[4]

A similar method was also used to kill hippopotamuses. David and Charles Livingstone (1865) described it in their *Narrative of an Expedition to the Zambezi and its Tributaries*, as seen in August, 1859, on the banks of the Shire River. 'Both banks are dotted with hippopotamus traps, over every track which these animals have made in going up out of the water to graze. The hippopotamus feeds on grass alone, and, where there is any danger, only at night . . . The hippopotamus trap consists of a beam five or six feet long, armed with a spear-head or hard-wood spike, covered with poison, and suspended to a forked pole by a cord, which, coming down to the path, is held by a catch, to be set free when the beast treads on it. Being wary brutes, they are still numerous'.

For killing smaller game, a falling log may alone be sufficient, as we see from the following account: 'Leopards are particularly fond of dogs, and the advantage of such a bait during the night consists in the certainty that the dog, finding itself alone in a strange place, will howl or bark, and thereby attract the leopard. . . . In Africa the natives form a trap by supporting the fallen trunk of a large tree in such a manner that it falls upon the leopard as it passes beneath to reach the bait. This is very effective in crushing the animal, but it is exceedingly dangerous, like all other African traps, as it would kill any person or other creature that should attempt to pass'.[5]

Again, C. Christy (1924), referring to the trapping in the Congo of the small antelopes known as duikers, wrote: 'Except in the villages, almost every native house has its little "runs" and "stops" formed of small sticks stuck in the ground close together, and leading up to a small drop-log trap with the log set almost horizontally, somewhere nearby in the grass, or in some neighbouring patch of gallery forest. . . . They are also caught with nets and snares. So common are they, that with suitable nets and dogs two or three natives with a skilled hunter can bring in a hundred or more skins a month'.

I have come across few other references to falling log traps but probably, being less dramatic than falling spears and guillotines, they may have attracted less attention from writers. In any case, animals can always learn to avoid traps, baited or unbaited, and it is evident

[4]Junker, 1892.
[5]Baker, 1890.

that such methods could be profitable only where game populations are high and unlikely to be seriously affected thereby.

Spears and missiles

The spear is the traditional weapon of primitive tribes throughout the world and the one most frequently used in Africa for hunting. The problem is not so much how to kill with a spear except, perhaps, in the case of elephants, as how to get close enough to do so. In general, one of three or four methods may be used. Animals can be stalked, chased on foot or horseback until they are exhausted or, if enough hunters are available, whole herds may be surrounded.

Spears too, are often used in combination with other weapons that I shall discuss later. Thus, the principal weapons of the Azande or Niam-Niam tribe in Zandeland are spears or lances, tipped with iron at the point or with antelope horns, and the *trumbash*, a throwing missile shaped like a boomerang, made of wood or iron and used for flinging at hares, small antelope or birds. At the same time, 'many of the Niam-Niam, being forest negroes, carry bows and arrows. The latter are contained in a small quiver and are poisoned. Also all Niam-Niam carry a small knife with a blade like a sickle. When a Niam-Niam gets his money he at once buys only the one necessity of life: a bag of durra, the rest goes to the purchase of spears, because spears are the important trade goods in Zandeland. Forty spears will buy a very nice young woman, and all the lads save up for that luxury'.[6]

Congo pygmies normally hunt in groups of three or four. If they find a herd of elephants one attacks and, when the animal turns to run, the others rush in from several directions and likewise plunge spears or swords into its body. In some regions the hunter goes alone, on foot and equipped with a heavy-bladed spear. He wears no clothes to catch in thorns and other obstructions, and his body is smeared with dung to conceal the human scent. On finding a herd of elephants resting during the noonday heat, he stalks a chosen animal, taking advantage of wind and cover, until he is within three or four yards of its head. Then he bounds forward and spears it, darting away into the bush before it has time to retaliate.

A. L. Cureau (1915) gives these details of how the Negritos or pygmies of tropical Africa 'know how to creep noiselessly amid the underwood of the miry forest and take their stand upon the outer edge of the boughs broken in some thicket by the shoulders of the elephants, whose gigantic size is shown by the tufts of hair hanging upon the raphia thorns and by the muddy stems impressed upon the

[6]Millais, 1924.

trees when they brush against them. The little hunters half cover themselves with this dunghill of rotten leaves and worm eaten wood, where they wait long hours in the animal stench of the elephant hairs. When the dim light of morning or evening shows the clumsy outlines of the great pachyderms in the greenish glimmer of the bush, the little man lets the herd go by; but when he sees the last animal, the oldest elephant, which forms the rear-guard, the small hunter suddenly leaps between its legs, plunges a lance with a broad, barbed head into its belly, and then with a bound conceals himself behind a tree from the rage of the wounded giant. This is but the first act of the tragedy, for the elephant dies very slowly unless some vital organ has been reached by the first blow. Away dashes the monster through the forest, and its little enemy must needs follow its trail, sometimes for one day, sometimes for two, harassing it all along the way, and getting possession of it only at a great distance from the starting point. Then he must return to the village for reinforcements'.

On occasions, a hunter will sit in the branches of a tree, waiting for his prey to walk beneath: 'Another method of slaying the elephant is practised by some of the upper Dôr and Baer tribes: a strong lance, with a handle five feet in length, the extremity shaped like a club, diameter about four inches, is laden with a stone, fixed to it with cords, and plastered over with clay, the whole being made as heavy as it can be managed. With this instrument a negro, conversant with the noonday haunts of the elephants—invariably under the shade of large trees—ascends one of them, and, laying himself out on a branch, quietly awaits the arrival of his prey; and when one of them is directly under him, with all his force he sends the spear into his back or shoulders. When the blow has been well directed, the animal bounds about for a short time, increasing the wound by the oscillation of the spear, and thereby accelerating his death'.[7]

The Dinkas of Bahr el-Ghazal province, Sudan, until recently hunted white rhinos in a similar way, by means of a wooden frame under a tree, many miles from the nearest habitation. It consisted of an upright beam in the ground, about 12 feet from the bole of a growing tree, and a cross beam joining the top of the upright to the tree about 12 feet from the ground. A man sat above the cross piece on a small platform and speared the rhino as it walked underneath. A very big, heavy, elephant spear was used and was driven down into the backbone behind the shoulders of the passing animal. This type of hunting was done on moonlit nights during the rains. Rhinos are in the habit of walking along the same tracks every day or night. A track was therefore selected which passed conveniently near to a suitable shady tree and a frame built over the pathway. Branches and

[7]Petherick, 1861.

timber were then placed so as to form a camouflaged tunnel guiding the unsuspecting rhino beneath the waiting spearman. A rhino horn in that part of the world was worth as much as a bull, and a young man wanting to get married perhaps only needed one more bull to complete the bride price. The horns were made into clubs which were greatly prized because they did not break like the usual type of ebony club does in a fierce fight. Small pieces of horn were sometimes made into finger rings and ornaments to hang on bead necklaces. The horns were not used in medicine, but shavings were sometimes put into stale beer if a visitor arrived unexpectedly, as they made the beer bubble so that it looked freshly brewed and suitable for a guest.

Although the Nilotic people of Kenya have only hunted elephant somewhat unsuccessfully by means of traps, their neighbours, the Lango used to lay low many of these noble creatures each year. 'They approached them with great boldness, and implanted innumerable poisoned arrows and spears into the beast, until he looked like an enormous walking pin-cushion. Then they followed him for days and days, and even for a fortnight. Each time he stopped for rest they stuffed more pins into him, until partially poisoned, and partially exhausted, he dropped, and was soon made an end of. Of course, such a method was dangerous, and an elephant would sometimes kill several of his tormentors before he succumbed. The deftest stroke was one into the knee with a spear, for an elephant when wounded thus, is at once incapacitated. He cannot get away on three legs like any other animal, and unless his companions help him he is doomed. However, his friends are often ready to give a helping hand, and our commanding officer once saw two of them place themselves each side of a wounded one, and hustle him away'.[8]

The Ndorobo, who inhabit thick forests bordering the Mau Escarpment in Kenya, devised a peculiar weapon for hunting elephants. 'In shape it was something like the hammer of a cannon, the heavy head giving additional weight in dealing a blow. The thickened part held a weapon shaped like a dart or arrow; the sharp end of the dart was smeared with a deadly poison. When the terminal piece was in position the whole weapon measured about eight feet in length. With this spear the elephant was attacked at close quarters. The dart was driven into its body and, being loosely fixed, stuck in the animal while the handle of the harpoon remained with the hunter. Another dart was then placed in the handle and the operation repeated when circumstances were favourable. In making the thrust, the hunter endeavoured to stick the dart into the abdomen where the intestines lie'.[9] (See also p. 45.)

[8]Sykes, 1903.
[9]Bland-Sutton, 1911.

According to Sir Richard Burton, the explorer and writer: 'The elephant hunt is with the African a solemn and serious undertaking. He fortifies himself with periapts and prophylactics given by the mganga, who also trains him to the use of his weapon. The elephant-spear resembles our boarding-pike rather than the light blunt arm employed in war; it is about six feet long, with a broad tapering head cut away at the shoulders, and supported by an iron neck, which is planted in a thick wooden handle. . . . It is not a little curious that the East African, though born and bred a hunter, is, unlike almost all barbarians, as skill-less as an European in the art of el asr, the "spoor" or "sign". The hunting-party, consisting of fifteen to twenty individuals, proceeds before departure to sing and dance, to drink and drum for a consecutive week. . . . When thoroughly drenched with drink, the hunters set out early in the morning, carrying live brands lest the fire should fail them in the jungle, and applying them to their mouths to keep out the cold air. . . . The great art of the African muinzi or elephant-hunter is to separate a tusker from the herd without exciting suspicion, and to form a circle round the victim. The mganga, then raising a shout, hurls or thrusts the first spear, and his example is followed by the rest. The weapons are not poisoned, they are fatal by a succession of small wounds. The baited beast rarely breaks, as might be expected, through the frail circle of assailants : its proverbial obstinacy is excited; it charges one man, who slips away, when another, with a scream, thrusts the long stiff spear into its hind quarters, which makes it change intention and turn fiercely from the fugitive to the fresh assailant. This continues till the elephant, losing breath and heart, attempts to escape; its enemies then redouble their efforts, and at length the huge prey, overpowered by pain and loss of blood trickling from a hundred gashes, bites the dust'.[10]

It is clear that elephant-hunting involved important ceremonies and, in addition to providing food and ivory, was probably of considerable sociological significance to the tribes that indulged in it.

J. Petherick (1861), British Consul in Khartoum, gave the following account of an elephant hunt in Bahr el-Ghazal, Sudan. It indicates the skill and courage required. One of the hunters, 'making one more bound forward, threw his lance, and hit the elephant on the foot, a feat entitling him to the animal's tusks. Retiring quickly as they had advanced, the infuriated beast withdrew the lance with his trunk, and, screeching with rage, he broke it in two, and darted at the party who had injured him. At the same time the negroes, watching the event, made a simultaneous attack on his left side, which they pierced with their lances, and succeeded in drawing him off towards them from the object of his rage; this was no sooner undertaken than his

[10]Burton, 1860.

right side was similarly pierced by half-a-dozen lances, thrown with such force that they penetrated to the socket. The maddened animal stood for an instant still, sqirting water on his wounds from his trunk, extracting some of the lances and breaking them; while so engaged he was subjected to renewed attacks, until, losing patience, he bolted off at a hard trot with several of the lances sticking in his body. He was however again brought to bay and, after repeated attacks, was overcome'.

About August 1819, Chaka, King of the Zulus, organised a great Royal hunt on a scale never before attempted. His plan was to encircle the game between the Black and White Umfolozi Rivers, south west of the present Umfolozi and Hluhluwe game reserves, and drive it into the trap formed by their junction. The river banks and all fords were strongly guarded and deep game pits dug beside the river. These were about 9 ft deep, 6 ft wide and 12-15 ft long. Their sides were sheer, but they had no sharpened stakes in them. Thorn fences formed funnels leading to the pits which were disguised with a covering of branches, reeds and grass. Beyond them was a light fence, intended to screen the hunters, which also contained funnels and runways so that any game escaping the pits would have to run the gauntlet of the spurs of the hunters.

Chaka forbade the use of poisoned spears for he was brave and thought them unmanly. Instead, he gave orders that elephants were to be hamstrung. Several of them mistrusted the apparent safety of the causeways covering the game pits and, instead, broke through the thorn fences and by-passed the hunters who rushed in to the attack. Many elephant, buffalo and rhino were killed as well as quite a few Zulu soldiers. Only two giraffe were killed, one in a game pit, one by spears, but innumerable kudu, water-buck, wildebeest, sable and roan antelope were slaughtered. Wild pig were met by parties of soldiers with dogs. The last arrivals were lion and leopards, preceded by jackals, hunting-dogs and hyaenas. Fierce fights took place with the lions and leopards after which all wounded game that had escaped were hunted by the dogs.

Some eight years later, 48 elephants were killed in a single drive in which massed spearing attacks were made after the animals had been surrounded. Hippopotamus were not hunted by the Zulus, however, who likened their meat to pork and would not eat it.[11] Matabele armies used also to surround herds of game animals and kill them with spears.

The people of Darfur used to hunt elephant on horseback, having 'singled out a straggler from the herd; or aim at him with spears from the trees; or make pits into which he falls'.[12] And, according to J. H.

[11]Ritter, 1955.
[12]Browne, 1799.

Speke (1864), the Somali 'from their roving habits of life, are as keen and cunning sportsmen as any in the world. They told me of many dodges they adopted for killing elephants, ostriches, and gazelles, which they do as follows: if an elephant is ever seen upon the plains, a large body of men assemble on foot, armed with spears, bows and sharp double-edged knives, with one man mounted on a white horse, to act as a teaser. This man commences by riding in front of the animal, to irritate and absorb his entire attention by riding in repeated circles just in front of him. When the huge beast shows signs of distress by fruitlessly charging on his nimble adversary, the footmen rush in upon him from behind, and hamstring him with their knives, and then with great facility soon despatch him with their arrows and spears.

Lord Dewar was witness to an interesting hunt in 1923, when, from the deck of his steamer, he watched for twenty minutes a small party of Shilluk warriors attacking an old buffalo bull. They worked him in exactly the same way as the Spanish bull-fighters, only with even greater skill and bravery. One man induced the bull to charge and, at the last moment, endeavoured to bury his spear in its chest, whilst supporters on either side rushed in and made a flank attack. There were many narrow escapes, but so regular and good was the work of the flankers that the man who provoked the charge was always rescued just as he appeared to be in a hopeless position. At last one flanker got in a heart stab with his long spear, and all was soon over.[13]

In his book, *Game Animals of the Sudan* (1931), from which the following extracts are quoted, Captain H. C. Brocklehurst, then game warden, gives precise details of hunting methods in that country. 'The Red Sea tribes who hunt on foot, drive herds of Ibex up a narrow gully until the animals are forced to walk in single file. Natives, previously concealed behind rocks, pelt them with stones, and later kill the cripples with knives. Wild sheep, similarly driven from one hill to another, are brought to bay in the intervening valley by dogs and slain with the spear. The rams, who are capable of defending themselves, generally escape and only the ewes and lambs are killed. This leaves a preponderance of rams over ewes, a condition which invariably leads to the ultimate extermination of any species, and for this reason the Barbary Sheep is gradually becoming extinct in inhabited areas. Whole herds of Antelope, generally the Kob, are driven to swim the river by the Upper Nile natives. They are killed with the spear by others of the tribe, who wait in boats under the river-bank.

[13]Millais, 1924.

'Kudu, Roan Antelope, Ariel and occasionally Tiang, Waterbuck and Hartebeest, are hunted with dogs. In the rainy season, when the deep going lessens their chance of escape, they are sometimes caught in the muddy ground, surrounded by numbers of natives on foot, and finished with the spear. The Buffalo is so difficult an animal to kill, and the value of his meat and hide being proportionately so small to the risks and dangers of the chase, that it is rarely he is attacked, and then only for the sake of the reputation which attaches to success. On the other hand, the Elephant, whose meat and ivory is highly prized and of great market value, is not similarly immune. The hunt often entails the definite sacrifice of horses, which rarely survive any period in the tsetse-fly areas, where elephant are usually found. . . .

'The lion is only hunted as a defensive measure. So long as he confines his attention to game, he is accorded due respect and left severely alone. But once he begins to apply his strength and cunning to the killing of native cattle, he becomes an expensive pest to be destroyed as rapidly as possible. When such a lion appears in certain districts, local natives combine to take action in an organised hunt. The active inhabitants of several villages, some mounted and all armed with spears, surround the spot where the lion has been located. Those mounted place themselves so that they can take advantage of their superior height and mobility and observe when the lion breaks cover. This he does several times before he makes a final stand. Then realising he is surrounded, he charges the unbroken ring of natives, to meet his death on their spears. It is rare for the attackers to escape without injury, and several usually receive wounds which they wilfully neglect for the sake of conspicuous and coveted scars. . . .

'Natives from West Africa, passing through or temporarily residing in the Sudan, are sometimes met using the bow and arrow. It is exceptional to find one who kills antelope, but many are expert shots and clever stalkers. A common ruse of theirs is to mount the stuffed carcase of a Ground Hornbill as a head-dress and, thus disguised, crawl through the grass towards their quarry. The "throwing stick" is a favourite weapon in certain parts of the Western and Central Sudan. It consists of a flat crescent-shaped piece of wood three feet in length and sharpened on both curves. It is used for the destruction of nothing larger than the guinea-fowl or that much relished delicacy expressly forbidden by the Koran, the hare. . . .'.

Two methods of killing gazelles in Somalia were described by the explorer J. H. Speke (1864). Two men would ride round the animals in large, but gradually diminishing circles, gradually manoeuvring them close to a bush in which a third was concealed so that he could shoot them with his bow and arrow.

'The other plan for killing them is extremely artful, and is done on horseback, and therefore on the open plain. Fleet animals, like antelopes and gazelles, always endeavour to head across their pursuers, no matter in which direction they go. The Somalis, therefore, taking advantage of this habit, when they wish to catch them on ponies, which are not half so swift as the gazelles in fair open chase, economise their strength by directing their animals' heads towards the leading gazelle, and thus inducing the herd, as they continue heading on, to describe double the circumference of ground their ponies have to traverse. In process of time, the gazelles, by their extra exertions, begin to flag and drop, and the hunters rush in upon them, and cut them up in detail'.

On another page, Speke wrote: 'When out shooting specimens, I often saw the Somali chasing down the Salt's antelopes on foot. I killed many of them myself right and left, when running like hares, with common shot, much to the astonishment of the Somali, for they are too small a mark for their bow and arrow shooting. The little creatures cannot stand travelling in the midday sun and usually lie about under favouring trees which line the water courses. Knowing this weakness, the cunning Somali hunter watches him down from feeding to his favourite haunts, and, after the sun shines strong enough, quietly disturbs him; then, as he trots away to search for another shady bush, they follow gently after to prevent his resting. In the course of an hour or so, the terrified animal, utterly exhausted, rushes from bush to bush, throwing itself down under each in succession until at length it gets captured'.

A. L. Cureau (1915), who described various types of traps and harpoons for killing elephant, hippos and wild oxen, mentioned an unusual method of attracting smaller game: 'The antelopes' timidity and swiftness make it a difficult prey, but the tribes who inhabit districts covered with jungle (the Kakas), where a battue is impracticable, know how to attract it within distance of the assagai by means of a call which they insert in the nose'.

A cunning device used in South Africa for escaping the attacks of formidable animals was described by Burchell (1824). It consisted of a number of black ostrich feathers 'tied round a thin stick of the size of the shaft of a hassagay, which is thus covered for two or three feet along the upper part of its length; their points turning outwards. This *feather-stick* often renders the natives an important service when hunting or attacking the larger and more ferocious wild animals. If in approaching too near, these creatures should suddenly turn upon them, their only chance of escaping, is by immediately fixing the feather-stick into the ground, and taking to flight. As this apparatus is always carried in a manner to be most conspicuous, the animal seeing it standing up beside him, mistakes it for the man himself, and

vents his fury upon it : by this stratagem the man gains time, either
to escape to a place of safety, or till his companions come up to his
assistance. In this manner the life of one of my Hottentots was once
saved from an enraged rhinoceros'.

Hamstringing

One of the difficulties in hunting big game such as elephant with
spear or sword lies in preventing escape of the quarry before it can
be killed. For this reason several native tribes as already mentioned,
resorted to the practice of hamstringing, the most dramatic accounts
of which are probably those of Bruce (1790) and Burton (1867).
Although the method varied in different places the principle was the
same. One hunter would attract the elephant's attention while others
would either hamstring it or plunge a sword or spear into its entrails.
As recently as the beginning of the present century, as many as 800
elephants were killed annually in this way by the Rizigat and
Hamman Arabs.

The explorer, James Bruce (1790), who discovered the source of the
Blue Nile gave this picturesque description of the hunting methods
of the Nubian *agageers*[14] that he witnessed shortly after he had
reached the source of the Blue Nile. 'As soon as the elephant is found
feeding, the horseman rides before him as near his face as possible; or,
if he flies, crosses him in all directions crying out, "I am such a man
and such a man; this is my horse and that has such a name; I killed
your father in such a place, and your grandfather in such another
place, and I am now come to kill you; but you are an ass in comparison of them". This nonsense he verily believes the elephant under-
stands, who, chased and angry at hearing the noise immediately
before him, seeks to seize him with his trunk or proboscis, and, intent
upon this, follows the horse everywhere, turning and turning round
with him, neglectful of making his escape by running straight
forward, in which consists his only safety. After having made him
run once or twice in pursuit of the horse, the horseman rides close up
along-side of him, and drops his companion just behind on the off-
side; and while he engages the elephant's attention upon the horse,
the footman behind gives him a drawn stroke just above the heel, or
what in man is called the tendon of Achilles. This is a critical moment;
the horseman immediately wheels round, and takes his companion
up behind him, and rides off full speed after the rest of the herd, if
they have started more than one; and sometimes an expert Agageer
will kill three out of one herd. If the sword is good, and the man not

[14]According to Capt. C. R. S. Pitman the word is probably a corruption of
bagheera, i.e. the Bagheera Arabs who still occupy that part of the country
(Carrington, 1958). See, however, p. 148.

afraid, the tendon is commonly entirely separated; and if it is not cut through, it is generally so far divided, that the animal, with the stress he puts upon it, breaks the remaining part asunder. In either case he remains incapable of advancing a step, till the horseman returning, or his companions coming up, pierce him through with javelins and lances; he then falls to the ground, and expires with the loss of blood'.

'Dextrous, too, as the riders are, the elephant sometimes reaches them with his trunk, with which he dashes the horse against the ground, and then sets his feet upon him, till he tears him limb from limb with his proboscis; a great many hunters die this way. Besides this the soil, at this time of the year, is split into deep chasms, or cavities, by the heat of the sun, so that nothing can be more dangerous than the riding'.

In Sir Richard Burton's account, 'three *aggageers* came galloping across the sand like greyhounds in a course, and judiciously keeping parallel with the jungle they cut off his retreat and turning towards the elephant; they confronted him, sword in hand. . . . In the way of sport, I never saw anything so magnificent, or so absurdly dangerous. No gladiatorial exhibition in the Roman arena could have surpassed this fight. The elephant was mad with rage and, nevertheless, he seemed to know that the object of the hunters was to get behind him. This he avoided with great dexterity, turning as it were upon a pivot with extreme quickness, and charging headlong, first at one and then at another of his assailants, while he blew clouds of sand in the air with his trunk and screamed with fury. Nimble as monkeys, nevertheless, the *aggageers* could not get behind him. . . . It was only by the determined pluck of all three that they alternately saved each other, as two invariably dashed in at the flanks when the elephant charged upon the third, upon which the weary animal immediately relinquished the chase and turned upon his pursuers. . . .'.

The same method was used for hunting the rhinoceros: 'The two rhinoceros were running neck and neck, like a pair of horses in harness, but bounding along at tremendous speed within ten yards of the leading Hamran. This was Taher Sherif, who, with his sword drawn, and his long hair flying wildly behind him, urged his horse forward in the race, amidst a cloud of dust raised by the two huge but active beasts that tried every sinew of the horses. . . . With the greatest exertion of men and horses we could only retain our position within about three or four yards of their tails—just out of reach of the swords. On they flew, sometimes over open ground, then through low bush, which tried the horses severely; then through strips of open forest, until at length the party began to tail off and only a select few kept their places. . . . One effort more and the sword flashed in the sunshine, as the rearmost rhinoceros disappeared in the thick screen

Rhinoceros hunt. From S. W. Baker (1867).

of thorns. . . . Taher Sherif shook his bloody sword in triumph . . . but the rhinoceros was gone. He could not reach the hamstring, as his horse could not gain the proper position. . . .'.[15]

Sir Samuel Baker (1890) has also commented on hamstringing as a way of crippling game: 'The Hamran sword-hunter is a merciless but wonderful horseman, and should three or four of these fellows form a party, they will frequently kill seven or eight giraffes during one hunt. The long and extremely sharp blade is exactly suited to this kind of sport, as the hocks of the giraffe are so high above the ground that they can be reached by the sword without the necessity of stooping. The speed of the horse is naturally imparted to the weapon, therefore when riding alongside, upon the left of the flying animal, the slightest blow will sever the hamstring, and all further movement is impossible. If the giraffe moved like ordinary quadrupeds, it could continue upon three legs, but the fact of its moving the legs of each side simultaneously renders it entirely helpless when one has been disabled'.

In most parts of the world, a brave and successful hunter is regarded with honour and respect. 'In the Somali country, as amongst the Kafirs, after murdering a man or boy, the death of an elephant is considered *the* act of heroism: most tribes wear for it the hair-feather and the ivory bracelet. Some hunters, like the Bushmen of the Cape, kill the Titans of the forests with barbed darts carrying Waba-poison. The general way of hunting resembles that of the Abyssinian Agageers described by Bruce. One man mounts a white pony, and galloping before the elephant, induces him, as he readily does—fire-arms being unknown—to charge and "chivy". The rider directs his course along, and close to, some bush, where a comrade is concealed; and the latter, as the animal passes at speed, cuts the back sinew of the hind leg, where in the human subject the tendon Achilles would be, with a sharp broad end knife. This wound at first occasions little inconvenience: presently the elephant, fancying, it is supposed, that a thorn has stuck in his foot, stamps violently, and rubs the scratch till the sinew is fairly divided. The animal, thus disabled, is left to perish wretchedly of hunger and thirst'.[16]

Describing native hunting methods in the Sudan, Captain H. C. Brocklehurst (1931) wrote: 'The Baggara, or cattle-owning Arab, who usually hunts on horse-back, dismounting only for the final combat, never allows his spear, a long flat-bladed weapon which will cut as well as pierce, to leave his hand. The southern Sudani and Nilotic Nago, whilst employing on occasion a similar but narrower weapon, more usually reverts to the short thin throwing spear, sometimes

[15]Burton, 1867.
[16]Burton, 1856.

barbed at the head and effective up to 50 or 60 yards. The object of
the former is to bring to bay an animal galloped to a standstill: the
latter either stalks his quarry up to throwing distance or, standing
concealed, has the animal driven towards him by beaters. The
Elephant, Hippo, Giraffe and most varieties of Antelope, and the
Ostrich, before he was placed on the protected list, are accounted for
in this manner. The White Oryx, who meets a typical death of this
sort was, up to twenty years ago, fairly common in Kordofan and
Dongola, but at the present time it is doubtful if a single herd exists
in Kordofan.

'The fact that hundreds of Oryx were destroyed annually by the
local nomads is probably not the whole reason for their disappearance.
They have been driven out by the extension of the grazing area of
camel-owning nomads'.

Oryx are hunted in drought years when they are driven by food
shortage from the northern desert. 'A present-day hunting party
consists of four to six camels, four or five men and two horses, the
latter being accustomed to drink only every second day. In the early
morning three men, a water-carrying camel and the two horses travel
either until a herd is sighted or new tracks met. They halt until, in
the heat of the day, the Oryx are resting under the trees. With
reasonable care they are comparatively easy to approach, but once
the hunter is seen or winded, the animals run a considerable distance
before settling down again. As soon as the herd stampedes, the men
start off at a gallop, keeping it at the best pace and in sight. After a
few miles a well-marked man can easily come up with them, if the
going is good; but this is not generally done. The object being the
destruction of as many as possible, the chase is continued at a
moderate pace for four or five miles, so that the horses are spared and
the whole herd exhausted. The heavy bulls, becoming more easily
blown, are usually in the rear. The horsemen close in, each picks out
a bull, dismounts and approaches on foot, the spear being held out
well in front.

'The Oryx, who invariably shows fight and is extremely dangerous,
charges with his head down, thrusting his horns to either side with a
scythe-like movement and emitting through his nostrils his curious
challenge. A few well-directed jabs and the animal's eyes are soon
pierced. Once blinded and the hamstrings cut, the maimed animals
are left and the hunters, mounting their horses, proceed a few hundred
yards and come up with the rest of the herd. The procedure is repeated,
and as the hunt ceases only when the horses are exhausted, as many
as ten Oryx may be killed. . . . The nomad Arab finds the Addax, an
animal living under similar conditions to the Oryx but further north,
an easier though less valuable quarry. Without the speed and stamina

of the larger animal, his only defence is his greater independence of water, and his consequent ability to exist in more remote districts. Still, the occasional traveller in Dongola and northern Darfur will find the sun-bleached skulls and bones, which tell their own story. . . . The Giant Eland, which in spite of its size and horns appears to be incapable of self-defence, is even less difficult to kill than the Addax, as an agile hunter can, without much difficulty, run down a heavy bull on foot. It is fortunate that this extremely local species is not greatly prized.

'The Giraffe, from the Baggara Arab point of view is placed only second to the Elephant as regards importance, and is the most coveted animal in the Sudan. . . . He is always hunted with horses, and one that is capable of being ridden in to a giraffe (most are naturally terrified) is always in demand, and has a local reputation equal to that of a winner of a classic race in England. Given a fit horse and a rideable country, the riding down and killing of a giraffe would be no great feat of skill or endurance, and were it not for the fact that he is capable of travelling for a considerable distance at a great pace, over ground and through thorn-trees impossible for a horseman to follow, he would, long ago, have been exterminated in the Baggara countries. . . . A giraffe will take his hunter many miles, and it is not until the ground is suitable to close in and force the pace that he becomes exhausted. Finally, he stands at bay using his forelegs against his enemy, who must exercise considerable care and agility to avoid injury. It is not long before both hamstrings are cut and he is killed by a spear-thrust in the front of his chest. . . .'.

Hippopotamus harpoons

For hunting hippopotamus an harpoon was usually employed, because the wounded animal would otherwise sink to the bottom of the water and be lost. Hippos used to be killed regularly on Lake Nyasa with large, barbed harpoons coated with poison. These were attached to ropes and thrown from canoes. Alfred J. Swann (1910) who travelled in Central Africa during the years 1882-1909 mentioned that hippos abounded and their fat was on sale in all the local markets. On one occasion he accompanied an expedition in a canoe containing eight men, three of whom swam to a herd to tease the animals. When they dived, the men raced back to the canoe. A hippopotamus that rose where they had been was greeted with shouts of derision. The enraged animal then flung its head over the side of the canoe whose crew reacted instantly. 'All except two jumped to the opposite side to counterbalance the weight; these two dug sharp spears into the softer part of the animal's neck; another hit him over the nose with an axe. This was to make it impossible for him to close the nostril, so that he could not keep under water. His attack had been rather too sudden, for he succeeded in pressing the gunwale under, and the canoe filled, pitching the lot of us into the water'.

Sir Samuel W. Baker (1890) gave the following vivid account of hippopotamus hunting by the Hamran Arabs and other tribes that used harpoons for the purpose: 'When a small herd of these animals are floating upon the surface, looking half-asleep in the midday sun, a couple of hunters enter the river about 200 yards up-stream, and swim cautiously with the current in their favour until they arrive within 5 or 6 yards of the nearest hippo. They hurl the harpoons simultaneously, and at the same instant they dive beneath the surface, and swim in an opposite direction, making direct for the nearest shore. The hippo, if well struck, is fixed by two harpoons, to each of which a rope is attached. A float of exceedingly light wood, the size of an ordinary man's head, is secured to the extremity of each rope, and these are arranged in lengths proportional to the maximum depth of the river, generally about 30 feet. When the hippopotamus feels the wound, it immediately plunges to the bottom, and rushes madly to and fro until it again rises to the surface to take breath. It at once perceives the large float at the extreme end of the line, and, frightened at the unaccustomed object, it seeks the concealment of the bottom. In the meantime the hunters have safely landed and are joined by their numerous companions, well provided with long ropes, and armed with spare harpoons and well-sharpened lances.

'The difficulty of capturing the hippopotamus would at first sight appear most formidable, but a very clever, though simple, plan enables the hunter to secure the float which is fastened to the harpoon line. The river may be about 150 yards in width. One of the hunters swims across, or wades if he can find a shallow ford, about 100 yards above the spot where the float upon the surface denotes the place beneath which the hippo is hidden in the river's depths. The man who crosses over takes the end of a long rope. This is more than sufficient to reach from bank to bank, and either end is now in possession of a howarti (hippo-hunter). An exceedingly strong but a lighter line is fastened to the centre of the rope, which is now stretched across the river, and the end of this second line is held by the same man who holds the superior rope; thus, upon one shore a man holds one end only, while upon the other shore his companion holds the extremities of two lines, one being fastened to the *middle* of the larger or main rope. It may be easily understood that the angle may be increased or decreased simply by widening the base through an extension of the two ends of the lines.

'In this manner the two hunters advance upon either bank, dragging the rope upon the surface until they can touch the float

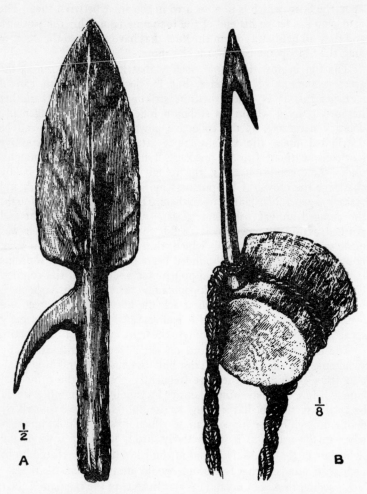

Harpoons used by natives for catching the hippopotamus. From
J. Bland-Sutton (1911).

which they intend to secure. They manipulate their lines in a manner that enables them to catch the float between the two ropes. When this is accomplished, the hunter on the opposite side of the river slacks off his rope, as his companion joins his two lines together and hauls upon the float, which is now secured in the angle between them. The man who has let go his end of the rope now rejoins his companions, and they all haul away upon the lines that have captured the float, to drag the hippopotamus towards the shore.

'The fun begins; the hippo, feeling that it is dragged, offers the greatest amount of resistance, but by degrees, and with careful management, it is guided within striking distance, and another harpoon is fixed within its stubborn hide. There is no longer any delicacy necessary, as the collective power of the hunters can be distributed upon the various ropes attached to their respective harpoons, without fear of breakage. I have seen a hippopotamus, under these conditions, quit the refuge of deep water and boldly challenge the crowd of his pursuers by landing upon the bank and making a general onslaught upon them. These splendid fellows fought the enraged animal with lances, some of which were caught and crushed within its powerful jaws. But the most telling defence was made with handfuls of sand, which, thrown in the prominent eyes, immediately forced the half-blinded beast to retreat to the welcome river, where it could wash, and prepare for a renewal of the conflict. Upon one occasion I saw a hippopotamus, which, when harpooned, had emerged from the river to attack the hunters, return over and over again to the charge, until it had smashed and broken so many spears that I was forced to terminate the fight by a bullet in its brain.

'The natives of Central Africa do not advance to the attack by swimming like the Hamran Arabs, but they harpoon the hippopotamus from canoes; and they are frequently upset by the infuriated animal before they have time to escape by paddling. Swimming would be a safer method of harpooning, as the hunter can save himself by diving, unseen by the hippopotamus, which invariably looks upwards when in the water, as it instinctively directs its vision towards the light; but in the White Nile and in the lakes there are crocodiles in such great numbers that few people would presume upon the risk'.

According to A. L. Cureau (1915): 'In spite of the elephant's great size, it is not as dangerous to hunt as the hippopotamus, and, above all, the wild ox. The people of the Middle Congo have invented a sort of harpoon for hippopotamus-hunting. Its head, which is large and barbed, comes away from the shank, but remains attached to it by a long cord. The shank is buoyed up by a float, which shows the position of the victim; for a wounded hippopotamus dives under water, sinks to the bottom, and only reappears on the surface when swollen by the gases of putrefaction'.

The Ethiopians around Lake Tana also used harpoons with detachable ends. The latter were made of wood 18 inches in length, with a barbed iron head $2\frac{3}{4}$ inches long by $1\frac{1}{2}$ inches broad. For $8\frac{1}{2}$ inches below the barb it was thickly coated with a black-coloured poison made by boiling the root of some tree. The shaft was of heavy wood 8 feet long and 4 inches in circumference; one end was split and a hole bored in it, into which 6 inches of the harpoon were let and kept in position by a binding made of twisted gut, which could be quickly tightened or loosened. For safety, except when in sight of their game, the barbed head was always kept covered by a sheath made of rush.[17]

The methods used by Shilluk hippopotamus hunters of the Upper Nile are described by John Millais (1924). After finding a hippo path leading from the water to the land and regularly used, 'One man lies in the reeds beside it all night, and as the great pachyderm comes ashore to feed, he dashes in and drives his spear home, retreating as the animal rushes back to the water. As a rule the "hippo" does not go far, so there is the float [of ambatch reeds tied to the harpoon] in the river to show the hunter his whereabouts next morning. Then follows a hunt which may last a couple of days, till the game is worn out and is speared with lances, but in this part of the river [near Kosti] there is often a white man with a rifle who will go to the assistance of the hunters and kill the "hippo" when he shows on the surface'.

A similar method of spearing hippopotamus was described by Andersson (1856) among the natives on the Teoge and other rivers to the northward of Lake Ngami in Bechuanaland. 'As soon as the hippopotamus is struck, one or more of the men launch a canoe from off the raft, and hasten to the shore with the harpoon-line, and take a "round turn" with it about a tree or bunch of reeds so that the animal may either be "brought up" at once, or, should there be too great a strain on the line, "played" (to liken small things to great) in the same manner as the salmon by the fishermen. But if time should not admit of the line being passed round a tree, or the like, both line and "buoy" are thrown into the water, and the animal goes wheresoever he chooses'. In this case he was followed by the other canoes and speared whenever he surfaced.

Almost exactly the same methods of hunting hippopotamuses were practised by the ancient Egyptians and have been described by Diodorus amongst others. They have evidently been employed for many hundreds of years without ever endangering the stock.

[17]Powell-Cotton, 1902.

Pitfalls

Pitfalls have been used from time immemorial to trap African game: they are probably the oldest known form of animal trap. A stone-age engraving in the Font-de-Gaume cavern in France shows the outline of a mammoth on which has been superimposed an enigmatical tectiform device which probably represents some form of trap.[18] Pliny[19] wrote of elephant traps, adding a picturesque legend which has no factual basis: 'In Africa they take them in pit-falls; but as soon as an elephant gets into one, the others immediately collect boughs of trees and pile up heaps of earth, so as to form a mound, and then endeavour with all their might to pull it out.'

Pitfall traps are usually constructed on some well-known animal tracks such as the approaches to a drinking place. They have smooth, sloping sides and are covered with branches and a layer of earth. Some are furnished with spikes at the bottom; others converge below ground level so that the legs of the trapped animal are pinned together and escape becomes impossible.

The Ndorobo, who shoot birds and the Colobus monkey with poisoned arrows, obtain larger mammals by digging narrow pits across their tracks. These pits are prepared at various angles and the game driven towards them: the animals stumble into the narrow pits and fall, breaking their legs and sometimes their backs. The largest animals are caught in regular game pits.[20]

Paul Kollmann (1899) described as follows the hunting methods of various tribes around Lake Victoria: 'Large stretches of the savanna land, so rich in wild animals, are enclosed with thorn hedges, in which openings are left here and there. In front of these openings a long trench is dug lengthwise, and covered with dry branches and grass. When an animal tries to get through an opening of this kind it breaks through the deceptive covering and falls into the trench. When it is taken in this way the hunter either spears it or kills it by cutting its throat. I also saw large hunting-nets with open meshes, which were stretched on stakes, just such as we use in marking out a district for driving game. The hunters do not generally venture to attack the numerous rhinoceroses, though they like eating the flesh, which is not unlike beef.

'In the extensive woods in the Ruwana Plain, as well as in Nata, the traveller often comes across small hunting-boxes and pitfalls for game. These are deep, narrow pits covered with thin brushwood dug in scattered places in the wood, or in great numbers to the right and to the left of the footpaths. On one occasion I counted over 200 in a

[18]Carrington, 1958.
[19]C. Plinius Secundus (A.D. 23-79) *Nat. Hist.* Bk VIII Ch. 8.
[20]Bland-Sutton, 1911.

half-hour's walk. In Nata I saw several such small pitfalls arrayed like a chessboard. Near the Ruwana River I saw a peculiar contrivance for catching game on a large scale. Two high walls of pilesades, pretty far asunder at first, gradually converge like a wedge leaving an exit at the narrow end. Just outside the exit numerous pitfalls covered with foliage were dug, and lay round in concentric semicircles, so that the game driven through the double hedge had to pass them, and naturally fell in. In addition, the Washashi[21] catch their game with large nets. Hippopotami are hunted with harpoons'.

A typically vivid account of the trapping of elephants in pitfalls was given by Sir Samuel Baker (1890). 'The night arrives, and the unsuspecting elephants, having travelled many miles of thirsty wilderness, hurry down the incline towards the welcome river. Crash goes a leading elephant into a well-concealed pitfall! To the right and left the frightened members of the herd rush at the unlooked-for accident, but there are many other pitfalls cunningly arranged to meet this sudden panic, and several more casualties may arise, which add to the captures on the following morning when the trappers arrive to examine the position of their pits. The elephants are then attacked with spears while in their helpless position, until they at length succumb through loss of blood'.

Captain H. C. Brocklehurst (1931) who has already been quoted in this chapter, listed various traps used in the Sudan by which more animals are killed than by any other means. These include the wheel trap[22] and the box trap composed of heavy boulders in the shape of a tunnel with doors at each end. These doors made of flat slabs are carefully balanced in an open position and fixed to a baited platform in the centre of the tunnel. If the bait is touched, the balance of the doors is upset and they fall into place. These traps are used in hill countries for the destruction of leopards, hyaenas and jackals.

Game pits were never used much by the Pambia who live in the hills between Tembura and Li Yubo in the southern Sudan. Instead, these people used to drive game up a hill which ended abruptly in a precipice. On the other hand, when a game reserve was proclaimed in 1949 at Bengengai in the Zande District, it took over two years before more than 2,000 pitfalls had been filled in. Indeed, in order to be effective, game pits have to be extremely numerous. 'Along the banks of the river about here [Victoria Falls] we found that the natives had dug a great number of pitfalls, about ten feet in depth, to entrap hippopotami, elephants, or buffaloes, which, being always placed in

[21]A tribe allied to the Masai. J. L. C-T.
[22]See p. 38.

the pathways made by the animals, are most difficult to detect, even when one knows there are such things about'.[23]

One of the reasons why so many pitfalls must be dug is that animals soon learn to avoid traps of all kinds. Thus, the sagacity of elephants at pitfalls is commented on by David and Charles Livingstone (1865). 'Elephants and buffaloes seldom return to the river by the same path on two successive nights, they become so apprehensive of danger from this human art. An old elephant will walk in advance of the herd, and uncover the pits with his trunk, that the others may see the openings and tread on firm ground. Female elephants are generally the victims: more timid by nature than the males, and very motherly in their anxiety for their calves, they carry their trunks up, trying every breeze for fancied danger, which often in reality lies at their feet. The tusker, fearing less, keeps his trunk down, and, warned in time by that exquisitely sensitive organ, takes heed of his ways'.

Some years later, P. H. G. Powell-Cotton (1902) found that the hippos of Lake Tana were no longer caught in pitfalls which were out of repair. 'The natives said the hippos had grown too cunning, and they no longer caught any in the traps, unless it might be a wounded animal, blinded with pain and fear, while bolting back to the water'.

The laborious communal effort required to dig large numbers of pitfalls, and to drive the game towards them, has rendered this method of trapping unpopular during recent years. There are simpler and more deadly means of achieving the same effect.

Footsnares

More efficient than pitfalls are footsnares. These are the oldest form of trap to be recorded and were depicted in a fresco of pre-dynastic age found at Hierakonpolis, Egypt. They probably date from Neolithic times and consist of a ring of pliable twigs resting above a shallow pit. From its periphery towards the centre are fixed numerous thin strips of wood, sharpened at the point and a noose of plaited hair or hide is laid on the ring and attached to a log of wood. The whole trap is then covered with sand. When an animal puts its foot into the snare, the ring clings to its leg and prevents the noose from slipping off. The encumbrance caused by the log then renders the animal vulnerable to spears or poisoned arrows. Footsnares of various sizes have been devised to catch game varying from elephant to duiker. Small pits, containing an iron spike, have often been used to lame animals so that they are unable to walk far and can afterwards be killed at leisure.

[23]Selous, 1881.

Bull elephant, Murchison, Uganda

Elephant displaying,
Luangwa, Zambia

Black rhinoceros,
Amboseli, Kenya

White rhinoceros,
Umfolosi, Zululand

The most graphic description of footsnares comes as usual from the pen of Baker (1890): 'The sure find for rhinoceros is in the neighbourhood of a peculiar red-barked mimosa. This is the much-loved food, and the appearance of the bushes will immediately denote the presence of the animal; they are clipped, as though by pruning shears, all the shoots being cut off in a straight line where the rhinoceros has been browsing. This neat operation is effected by the prehensile lip and the shear-like teeth. Another proof of rhinoceros will be found in the vast piles of dung, nearly always against the stem of a considerable tree; it is a peculiar custom of this animal to visit the same place every night, and this regularity of functions brings it into the traps which are cunningly devised by the natives for its capture.

'A round hole, the size of an ordinary hat-box, is dug near the tree. This is neatly formed, and when completed, it is covered with a wooden circle like the toy wheel of a child's waggon. The spokes are made of flat bamboo, with sharp points overlapping each other in the centre, in the place where the nave would be. This looks rather like a sieve when fitted carefully as a cover to the hole. If any person were to thrust his fist through this elastic substance, the points of the bamboo would prevent his hand from being withdrawn, as they would retain his arm. In the same manner this sieve-like cap would retain the leg of an animal, should it tread upon the surface and pass through. Accordingly a noose is laid upon the surface. The rope is constructed specially, of great strength, and the end is fastened to a log of wood that weighs about 200 or 300 lbs. This is buried slightly in the earth, together with the cord. A quantity of dung is thrown carelessly over the freshly turned ground to conceal the fact. The rhinoceros, like many other animals, has a habit of scraping the ground with its fore foot when it visits the nightly rendezvous; during this action it is almost certain to step upon the concealed trap. The foot sinks through, and in the withdrawal the noose fixes itself upon the leg, prevented from slipping off by the pointed support beneath, which remains fast, adhering to the skin.

'The moment that the rhinoceros discovers that its leg is noosed, it makes a sudden rush; this draws the noose tight, and, at the same time, the jerk pulls the buried log out of the trench. The animal, frightened at the mishap, gallops off, with the heavy log following behind. This arrangement is excellent, as it leaves an unmistakable trace of the retreat, which can easily be followed by the trappers on the following morning. At the same time, there is not the same risk of the rope breaking that would be occasioned by a steady pull. The log, which trails behind, catches in the innumerable bushes and thorns, causing great fatigue, until the rhinoceros, thoroughly wearied, is obliged to halt. When discovered by the hunters, it is

Following the noosed rhinoceros. From S. W. Baker (1890).

generally entangled by some attempt to turn, which has hooked the log around a tree; the fight then commences, as the beast has to be killed with spears, which penetrate the hide with difficulty. Accidents frequently happen when the rhinoceros, thoroughly enraged, succeeds in snapping the rope'.

My final example comes from H. Melladew (1909) who wrote about the Sudan in the year 1880. 'On the parched plains to the north we found nothing but giraffe, various kinds of antelope, and a few ostriches. The latter are sought after by native hunters who follow their employment singly, living for long periods of time alone in some part of the desert known to be frequented by those wary birds. Once I came upon one of these men, and found him sitting in a natural hut formed by a thickly overhanging bush, busily employed in making his ostrich traps. These consist of a ring, 9 inches or so in diameter, twisted from the split leaf stem of the dome-palm, through which all round, like the spokes of a wheel, a number of pointed spikes of the same material are passed, the tips almost meeting in the centre of the ring. These traps are laid on the ground and lightly covered with sand in places where ostriches are wont to congregate. Should a bird step upon such a trap, his heavy foot in the loose sand slips through the ring, the points clung again firmly upon the leg, which, thus encumbered by the whole trap, makes the ostrich a comparatively easy victim. Whether many are caught by this somewhat primitive contrivance I could not ascertain; the hunter, a bold old man, was a curious specimen of his kind; his only clothing was a narrow strip of leather round the loins, and a few beads encircling his neck; his sole companion a donkey, who fetched his weekly supply of water from the far-off water-hole; his only food some dry dhurra, his only arms a knife, spear, and shield'.

Nets and nooses

A method of hunting, employed mostly in forested regions such as parts of the Congo, is to fix a large net across an open space and, with a number of men, drive into it small game such as puku, oribi and reed buck. These are then stabbed with spears or shot with arrows whilst they are entangled. Loop nets are used by the Wanyamuezi to trap game.

In addition to their bows and poisoned arrows, the Mbuti pygmies use nets for hunting. In this case, they have to join together in bands: the males guard the nets and kill the animals driven into them by the women and children. The pygmies are completely adapted to life in the forests—unlike most races they do not try to control their environment but adapt themselves to it. Short of stature, with light skin and stocky bodies, they have inhabited the north-eastern Congo rainforest for at least 5,000 years and were referred to in Egyptian writings of the 6th Dynasty.

Among the cannibal Fan tribes of West Africa, elephant and other game were entangled in vines to check their flight till the hunters had time to kill them. These vines were woven into a kind of fence towards which the elephant was driven. 'The first idea of the animal is flight. He rushes ahead almost blindly, but is brought up by the barrier of vines. Enraged, and still more terrified, he tears everything with his trunk and feet. But in vain; the tough vines, nowhere fastened, give to every blow, and the more he labours, the more fatally he is held. Meantime, at the first rush of the elephant the natives crowd round; and while he is struggling in their toils they are plying him with spears, often from trees, till the poor wounded beast looks like a huge porcupine. This spearing does not cease till they have killed their prey'. So wrote Paul B. du Chaillu, famous for the discovery of the gorilla, in his book *Explorations and Adventures in Equatorial Africa* (1861). (p. 10)

Nets were made of various plant fibres worked by hand into a rope. Fibre from the bark of a baobab (tebaldi) tree was often used for this purpose. Where game is very abundant, enormous fences may be erected to keep elephant, eland, pigs etc. from fields and plantations. An opening is often left in these fences in which a game pit is dug and covered with grass. Not all central African tribes put sharpened stakes at the bottom of such pits, but fences are often used in this way.

In general, it seems that the use of nets for hunting is restricted to forested regions and, even here, is merely an adjunct to other kinds of trap. This point is made clear by the following quotation from T. H. Parke (1891) *My Personal Experiences in Equatorial Africa*, referring to the shores of Lake Albert Nyanza in 1889.

'The dwarfs set the net in the forest in the form of a semicircle; they then drive the game towards it, and, when within its curve, they shoot at them with their arrows—poisoned or otherwise. Pitfalls in the ground are also used for the purpose of catching game; they make large oblong holes in the earth, somewhat like an enlarged grave for the deposit of a human body and narrower below than above; they are arranged on some frequented game track and are constructed with great care and nicety. Each of these pits is covered over with small twigs over which leaves are strewn; so that the elephant, or other desired prey, may walk up to it unsuspectingly. When he steps on top of this, he, of course, drops in; and cannot by any possibility, extricate himself. Another method of killing game which they employ is by suspending a heavy beam, armed with a very strong spike of wood or iron, over a game trap. This thing is so arranged that when the animal, in walking along, breaks a vine stretched across the path, the upper end of the beam, previously secured by the distal end of this vine, is set free. . . .'.

Arrows and Poison

Most of the tribes of Central Africa use bows and arrows for hunting. Often, but not always, the arrows are poisoned. The klipspringer is a favourite quarry because, when disturbed, it retreats to a high peak or rock where, surrounded by dogs, it can be approached close enough to be shot. In Uganda the arrows are made of a reed, called "bango", 2 ft. long and bearing a 6 in. point of soft iron. Although most of the tribes do not feather their arrows, any more than do the Bushmen of South Africa, the Achikunda use vultures' wing feathers for this purpose. Two kinds of poison are prepared, one vegetable the other animal, and they kill quickly. Sometimes game is run to a standstill and then shot with non-poisoned arrows and the Bari of Equatoria province, Sudan, tackle buffalo in this way. Sir Richard Burton who, in 1856 was one of the earliest explorers to find his way into Tanganyika, spoke of coming across 'many tribesmen with full-sized bows and sheaths of grinded arrows whose black barbs and necks showed a fresh layer of poison'.

'One of the poisons employed by the tribes of the forest to smear their weapons, in order to make them more deadly, is a dark substance of the colour and consistency of pitch. It is supposed—if native women may be trusted—to be made out of a species of arum, a very common plant, with large leaves, found in any quantity between Fort Bodo and Indesura. Its smell, when fresh, reminds one of old blister plaster. That it is deadly there can be no doubt. They kill the elephants and other big game with it, as certainly as these animals could be slain with bone-crushing rifles'.[24]

According to David and Charles Livingstone (1865) buffaloes near Lake Nyassa were wary from being hunted with poisoned arrows. 'The arrow, making no noise, the herd is followed up until the poison takes effect, and the wounded animal falls out. It is then patiently watched till it drops—a portion of meat round the wound is cut away, and all the rest eaten. Poisoned arrows are made in two pieces. An iron barb is firmly fastened to one end of a small wand of wood, ten inches or a foot long, the other end of which, fined down to a long point, is nicely fitted, though not otherwise secured, in the hollow of the reed which forms the arrow shaft. The wood immediately below the iron head is smeared with the poison. When the arrow is shot into an animal, the reed either falls to the ground at once, or is very soon brushed off by the bushes; but the iron barb and poisoned upper

[24]Stanley, 1890.

part of the wood remain in the wound. If made in one piece, the arrow would often be torn out, head and all, by the long shaft catching in the underwood, or striking against trees'.

As I mentioned earlier, one continually comes across references to a multiplicity of different hunting and trapping methods being employed simultaneously by the same tribe, often against the same species of game. At the beginning of the century, for instance, the forest between Lake Kivu and Lake Edward 'was full of traps set by the Pigmies. The ordinary type was a bamboo bent towards the game path with a string fastened to the ground, where it was tied in a running noose: by this means, I am informed, they catch many pigs and small quadrupeds of the forest. They also fix spears, weighted with heavy blocks of wood, in the trees, and the elephant passing underneath releases the spear by breaking the cord with which it is attached; but I think their usual method of slaying elephant is by firing poisoned arrows into them, having done which, they follow the unfortunate beast for days, until he drops'.[25]

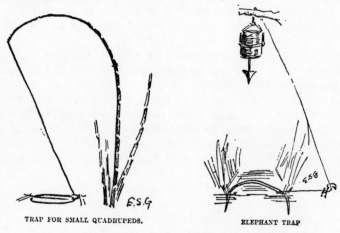

TRAP FOR SMALL QUADRUPEDS.   ELEPHANT TRAP

Game traps. From E. S. Grogan and A. H. Sharp (1900).

Some tribes living in districts rich in game never learned to hunt or trap, whilst others never had the opportunity. For example, P. Kollmann (1899) said that hunting is 'almost entirely unknown to the Msiba as game does not occur in the part of Kisiba near [Lake Victoria], but only in the western part of Mutatembwaland, where it borders the Kagera plain. The Wassindja hunt with bows and arrows. There is not very much game; at least, there is not much in the extensive forest. This forest is interrupted by good-sized stepp-like

25 Grogan & Sharp, 1900.

clearings, and in these many sorts of antelopes and rhinoceroses take up their abode'.

The Ndorobo people are also scattered over Masailand. During the last century they lived by hunting, chiefly elephant but also buffalo and antelopes. Joseph Thomson (1885) gives the following account of their methods. 'In hunting the elephant the Andorobbo use a peculiar weapon. In shape it is like the rammer of a cannon, the heavy head being intended to give additional weight in dealing a blow. In the thickened part is placed a weapon like a short but thick arrow, fifteen inches long, the head of the arrow being smeared with the deadly poison of the *murju*. The whole spear is little short of eight feet. With this the elephant is attacked at close quarters, the arrow part driven into the great brute, and being loosely fixed in the handle, it remains when the latter is withdrawn. Another arrow is then affixed, and the same operation performed. It is said that an elephant will live a very short time after being thus stabbed, and entire herds are killed without one escaping, so dexterous and daring are these hunters. The Andorobbo also use the ordinary bow and arrow, but only for the smaller game'. (See also p. 20.)

One of the earliest accounts of the hunting methods of the Bushmen comes from Sparrman (1785). 'There is another species of Hottentots, who have got the name of *Boshies-men*, from dwelling in woody or mountainous places. These, particularly such as live round about *Camdebo* and *Sneeberg*, are sworn enemies to the pastoral life. Some of their maxims are, to live on hunting and plunder, and never to keep any animal alive for the space of one night. . . . Their weapons are poisoned arrows, which, shot out of a small bow, will fly to the distance of two hundred paces; and will hit a mark with a tolerable degree of certainty, at the distance of fifty, or even a hundred paces. From this distance they can by stealth, as it were, convey death to the game they hunt for food, as well as to their foes, and even to so large and tremendous beast as the lion : this noble animal thus falling by a weapon which, perhaps, it despised, or even did not take notice of. The Hottentot, in the meantime, concealed and safe in his ambush, is absolutely certain of the operation of his poison, which he always culls of the most virulent kind; and it is said, he has only to wait a few minutes, in order to see the wild beast languish and die'.

W. J. Burchell (1824) has left us an account of the poison used by Bushmen to tip their arrows. 'This poison is obtained by inspissating the milky juice [of *Amaryllis toxicaria*], either by the heat of the sun, or, as I was told, by boiling. It is mingled with the venom of snakes, or a large black species of spider of the genus *Mygale*, and forms a half-viscous, gummy compound. In this state it is spread upon the heads of their arrows, and the direful and fatal effects of a wound made by them are the chief, and almost only, cause of that dread in which the *Bushmen* are held by every other inhabitant of Southern Africa. The ingredients of their *arrow-poison* vary according to the part of the country inhabited by them; as the same plant, or substances, are not to be found in every place: but the venom of serpents always constitutes an essential part. This shows how attentively the nation have studied the horrid art, and how well they understand the effect of their combinations: for they must have perceived that the poison of serpents operates in a manner different from that of vegetables, the former attacking the blood, while the latter corrupts the flesh. From such a wound, if the poison be fresh, there is little hope of surviving, unless it happen to have been made in some part of the body where all the surrounding flesh can be instantly cut out'.

In the Jipe area of Tsavo, poison is obtained by boiling roots and branches from selected *Acokantha friesiorum* trees. Only some trees are really poisonous and these are recognised by the presence of dead rodents, insects and other small animals round their roots.[26]

A stratagem employed by the Bushmen hunters for approaching Springbuck and other game has also been recorded by Burchell. It consisted of an unusually large fur cap 'made of spring-buck skin, of a shape extending far behind the head, and intended to have as much as possible the appearance of that animal's back. This was for the purpose of deceiving the game, and of enabling the wearer, as he creeps along between the bushes, to approach the animal within reach of his arrow. It is called a *be-creeping cap* (Bekruip-muts); and is only worn when in pursuit of game'.

In addition to inflicting poisoned wounds, the people of Africa have occasionally killed animals with poisonous food. Thus Speke (1863) mentioned that in Somaliland, one way of killing ostriches was by finding out what places they usually resorted to in search of food, and throwing down some tempting herb of strong poisonous properties which they eagerly ate and died from.

A second example is afforded by this account of the hunting methods of the Fan of West Africa, given by Mary Kingsley (1897): 'A certain percentage of ivory collected by the Fans is from live elephants, but I am bound to admit that their method of hunting elephants is disgracefully unsportsmanlike. A herd of elephants is discovered by rubber hunters or by depredations on plantations, and the whole village, men, women, children, babies and dogs turn out into the forest and stalk the monsters into a suitable ravine, taking care not to scare them. When they have gradually edged the elephants on into a suitable place, they fell trees and wreathe them very roughly

[26]Jenkins, P. (1956) *Oryx* 3, 323-6.

together with bush rope, all round an immense enclosure, taking care not to scare the elephants into a rush. This fence is quite inadequate to stop any elephant in itself, but it is made effective by being smeared with certain things, the smell whereof the elephants detest so much that when they wander up to it, they turn back disgusted. I need hardly remark that the preparation is made by the witch doctors. . . . Then poisoned plantains are placed within the enclosure, and the elephants eat them and grow drowsier and drowsier; if the water supply within the enclosure is a pool it is poisoned, but if it is a running stream this cannot be done. . . .'. After some days 'the best hunters steal into the enclosure and take up safe positions in trees, and the outer crowd set light to ready-built fires and make the greatest uproar possible, and fire upon the staggering terrified elephants as they attempt to break out. The hunters in the trees fire down on them as they rush past, the fatal point at the back of the skull being well-exposed to them. . . . One elephant hunt I chanced upon at the final stage had taken two months' preparation'. A hunt such as this must have been the most profitable and exciting event of the year for these people.

Drought and Starvation

The second method of catching ostriches that Speke described was not so easy, but managed with great effort. The birds cannot see at night to feed and they were followed all day by a Somali on a pony, to prevent them from eating. After three days or so, the birds become so weak that they could be ridden down and killed. The flesh was eaten and the feathers sent to the coast for sale.

Another example of animals being deprived of food is given by Frederick Selous (1881) the famous hunter, explorer and naturalist, who was killed in action in November 1917 at Beho-Beho, German East Africa (Tanganyika). Selous records that hippopotamuses were starved to death on the Umniati River near the Kariba Gorge: 'Of this journey there is but one circumstance to record, and that is our coming upon a party of Kafirs engaged in starving a herd of hippo-potami to death. The pool in which the poor brutes were enclosed was a large one, over two hundred yards broad and about four hundred in length. On the farther side, where the bank was low, a thick hedge which had been made all along the water's edge, behind which several temporary pools had been erected; above and below the pool, where the river ran in several streams amongst little bushy islands and rocks, strong dams had also been made and more huts erected. On our side of the river the bank was about twelve feet high and very steep, so that to get from the fatal pool was impossible for the poor prisoners, unless indeed they could muster up courage to make a rush and burst their way through one of the barriers, and this, even when in the last extremity of hunger, they do not appear ever to attempt. When we came to the pool there were still ten living hippo-potami in it; eight of these seemed to be standing on a bank in the middle of the water, as more than half their bodies were exposed; the poor brutes were all huddled up in a mass, each with his upraised head resting on another's body. It was a very pitiful sight; two more were swimming about, each with a very heavily-shafted assegai sticking in its back; these assegais are plunged into them at night when the starving beasts come near the fences seeking for a means of exit from their horrible prison'.

'The East African, who can seldom afford his longing for meat by slaughtering a cow or a goat, looks eagerly forward to the end of the rains, when the grass is in a fit condition for firing; then, armed with bows and arrows, and with runga or knobkerries, the villagers have a battue of small antelopes, hares and birds. During the hot season also, when the waters dry up, they watch by night at the tanks and pools, and they thus secure the larger kinds of game. Elephants especially are often found dead of drought during the hot season; they are driven from the springs which are haunted by the hunters, and, according to the Arabs, they fear migrating to new seats where they would be attacked by the herds in possession'.[27]

Crocodile hunting

The male crocodile produces four glands of musk, 'two of which are upon either side, beneath the jaws, and two upon either side of the groin. These are highly prized by the Arabs in the Soudan, where crocodile-hunting is pursued as a profession. . . . The crocodile is harpooned by the Arabs precisely in the same way as the hippo-potamus, with the exception that, instead of being struck when floating on the surface, the hunters swim under cover of the bank when they have descried a crocodile asleep upon a bed of sand; the harpoon is then cast, and as the crocodile immediately plunges into the river, the hunters with equal agility jump out. In many portions of the Soudan the hunters are armed with rifles, but the harpoon in dexterous hands is more effective as the creature seldom escapes. Great numbers of crocodiles may be shot, but very few in proportion are actually secured, as the body sinks immediately in deep water; and, unlike the hippopotamus, it will not rise to the surface for several days, until decomposition shall have set in, and the belly has become inflated with foul gas'.[28]

[27]Burton, 1860.
[28]Baker, 1890.

The Somalis of Jubaland today kill crocodiles by hitting them on the head with a heavy, long-handled hammer as they sleep on the sandbanks. There is a Somali legend that the riverine people rule crocodiles and can send them to kill their enemies.[29]

Major Gaetano Casati (1891) described the methods of the Bari crocodile-hunters in Equatoria as follows: 'The hunters, properly posted, on the banks of the river, gesticulating and throwing grain on the water, pronounce, with a loud voice, and in monotonous rhythm, the words appropriate to the ceremony. The crocodile, endowed with very sharp sight, leaves its hiding-place and gradually approaches the shore, at first timidly showing its nose, then its head. Some of the hunters then get cautiously into the river, and, approaching the creature at its sides, rapidly throw a rope with a noose over its head and round its neck. Immediately all precipitate themselves into the river, and, without giving their prey time to resist, they drag him out of the water and kill him on the shore'.

The crocodile is unjustifiably persecuted and certainly does not warrant its evil reputation, as we shall see in Chapter VI, yet the only explorers to express sympathy for the wretched animals appear to be David and Charles Livingstone (1865)[30] who wrote: 'Crocodiles in the Rovuma have a sorry time of it. Never before were reptiles so persecuted and snubbed. They are hunted with spears, and spring traps are set for them. If one enters an inviting pool after fish, he soon finds a fence thrown round it, and a spring trap set in the only path out of the enclosure. Their flesh is eaten and relished. The banks, on which the female lays her eggs by night, are carefully searched by day, and all the eggs are dug out and devoured. The fish-hawk makes havoc among the few ones that escape their other enemies'.

People living down the Blue Nile today say that whereas the majority of crocodiles are harmless, a few acquire the habit of feeding on domestic animals and may become a danger to man. It is interesting, therefore, to read the following remarks of J. H. Churi (1853): 'The crocodiles are of two kinds, and possess different habits. Some are fond of human flesh, others are not. In Upper Egypt they are very numerous but not so large as those of Nubia superior. They, nevertheless, are very large, and ferocious-looking animals. . . . The Nubians and Negroes derive two benefits from killing the crocodiles and the hippopotamus. They eat their exquisite flesh, and make their shields and corbage of their skins'.

---

[29]Ward, J. N. & Sorrell, D. S. (1950) Oryx 1, 26-34.
[30]Throughout my reading in the preparation of this book, I have been constantly impressed by the accuracy of Dr. Livingstone's observations and the perspicacity of his deductions.

In this chapter, I have outlined the main hunting methods evolved in Africa before the advent of Europeans. Often revoltingly cruel and varying widely in efficiency, they nevertheless provided the people with much-needed food, generally without endangering game populations. In the following chapters I shall attempt to contrast the devastating effects wrought more recently by fire-arms, steel wire, agriculture and introduced diseases on the wild animals of the African continent.

Hunting the gnu. From A. Sparrman (1785).

CHAPTER III

THE CHANGING SCENE

DESPITE the toll taken by African natives, the great herds of game encountered by the earliest European explorers bore ample testimony that man and beast were subsisting together in their chosen habitats, and that the primitive hunter in fact occupied an important niche in the natural order. It was not until the Europeans introduced fire-arms and, at a later stage, wire which poachers could use for snares, that the slaughter of game on a large scale really began. In the following chapter, we shall see how the scene then changed, the ever dwindling herds were pushed back before the advances of civilisation and a number of species exterminated in quick succession.

It is not easy, however, to get an unbiased, objective picture of recent changes in the populations of game animals in eastern Africa. Although there is no doubt that numbers have, indeed, been deplorably reduced, many modern writers, with the best of intentions, tend to exaggerate the situation. Even authoritative statements from experienced game conservation officers reflect two aspects of opinion. The following are examples:

'Three hundred years ago in South Africa there was a wild animal population totalling millions. Less than one hundred years back, even forty years ago, in East Africa were vast concourses of plains game which were a joy to behold. What is the situation today? Gone are the teeming herds of the past'.[1]

'It is encouraging to report that, except for some forms of less than specific rank, no animal of East Africa has become extinct and most species are still abundant. There is still time to save the interesting fauna in its natural habitat, provided reserves are chosen wisely.'[2]

These two statements do not conflict. The game of South Africa has certainly been almost entirely exterminated with the exception of small pockets in reserves and national parks. But, with the development of game ranching as an economic form of land use (Chapter X), even here the situation may greatly improve in the future. In East

[1]Captain Charles R. S. Pitman in a Paper read to the Mammal Society of the British Isles on 27th March, 1960.

[2]D. Foster-Vesey-Fitzgerald (1954) *Oryx* **2**, 1-17.

Africa the game has certainly been much reduced, but large concentrations still occur in certain places.

The narratives of many Victorian travellers create the impression that formerly the game of Africa darkened the horizon in all directions. But, when the missionary, J. L. Krapf (1860), travelled towards Mt. Kenya about 130 years ago, he remarked on the abundance of game only in much the same places as the traveller of today would see it. Dr. David Livingstone, who usually relied on the resources of the land, made special mention of the purchase of a goat as a great event after a long meatless period in Central Africa. So game could not have been abundant everywhere, even in his time.[3] With these points in mind, let us now examine some of the accounts of earlier travellers and try to obtain a true picture of the situation.

South and South-eastern Africa

From early records of white settlement of the Cape, it is clear that wild animals abounded in the immediate vicinity of Cape Peninsula. Hippopotamus, black rhinoceros, elephant and the large predators such as lion, leopard and wild dog, and antelopes such as eland, red hartebeest and steenbok roamed about in an area part of which is today the city of Cape Town.[4] On 24 April 1652, seventeen days after landing in Table Bay, Commander Jan von Riebeeck recorded in his diary the killing of a hippopotamus and later mentioned that hardly a day passed without the settlers having trouble from wild animals damaging their crops. F. Le Vaillant (1790) and other writers also give accounts of a very rich fauna.

Anders Sparrman (1785), a Swedish doctor who visited the Cape during 1772 to 1776, saw large numbers of red hartebeest and Cape mountain zebra near Bob River and herds of springbuck, red hartebeest and quagga on the plains of the Great Fish River. Of the quagga, now long extinct, he wrote: 'It is a species of wild horse, very like the *zebra*; the difference consisting in this, that the quagga has shorter ears, and that it has no stripes on its fore legs, loins, or any of its hind parts. . . . That these quaggas might be broken in for the saddle or harness, I have not the least doubt, as just before my departure for Europe, I saw one driven through the streets in a team with five horses; but with the zebra nobody has yet made any fair trial in this particular'.

But, he added, 'the lion, indeed, is now almost extirpated from this part of the country; though it sometimes happens, that one or two of them come hither farther from the northwards'. He mentioned that his moderation in not shooting more buffaloes than he required,

---

[3]D. Foster-Vesey-Fitzgerald *loc. cit.*
[4]Merwe, N. J. v.d., pp. 363-70 *in* Davis, D. H. S., 1964.

earned him a great deal of respect from many of the colonists as, 'they were very much discontented with the capricious conduct of several sportsmen, who, merely for the pleasure of shooting, are guilty of wasting the treasures of nature in the most unjustifiable manner; and by unnecessarily destroying the game, spoil their own sport in future, as well as that of others'.

Although many of the South African Dutch were merciless hunters, it is only fair to point out that within 25 years of the founding of the Cape, in 1652, Governor Simon van der Stel extended protection to certain species of game including hippopotamus, rhinoceros, buffalo and eland. Unfortunately, with the change of government at the beginning of the 19th century, these measures were relaxed to such an extent that many of these animals disappeared from their original habitats. Wild animals, especially the predatory kinds, caused great losses to farmers and President Paul Kruger in 1884 was the first to realise that protection of animals and plants could be practised effectively only by putting aside certain areas as reserves. This was half a century before the idea was applied in British-administered regions of Africa.[5]

In the following words, however, Sparrman indicated that even small antelopes were being persecuted fairly intensively in his time. 'The game here, and in the country about Constantia consists chiefly of small *antilopes*, as in *False-bay*, viz of *steenbocks*, the *antilope grimmia* of Pallas, and of *Klipspringers*, which, however, I have not had an opportunity of examining near; likewise of *diving goats*, so called from a peculiar manner they have of leaping and diving, as it were, under the bushes. The method of hunting these small antilopes is to drive them from their cover among the bushes, which is best done by hounds; at which time the sportsmen must take care to be ready with his gun. They are likewise caught with snares placed at the entrance into vineyards and kitchen-gardens. These snares are fastened to the top of an elastic branch or bough of a tree, one end of which is made quite fast in the earth, and the other being bent downwards, is attached very slightly to a board, which is laid on the ground, and covered with earth. It is farther so contrived, that when the animal treads on the board, this gives a little swing, upon which the elastic bough flies loose, and draws the snare over one or two of the animal's legs, at the same time lifting the creature up along with it into the air, so that it remains hanging there'.

Of the eland in South Africa, W. J. Burchell (1822) wrote on 14 September 1811 : 'We agreed to rest a day at this place, as well to refresh our teams as to give the people an opportunity of hunting *Elands*, of which a considerable number had been seen under the

[5]Merwe, N. J. v.d. *loc. cit.*

mountain. Those who remained by the waggons, were busily employed in cutting up the meat of four Elands, brought home the day before, into large slices generally less than an inch in thickness, which they hang on the bushes to dry. . . . All the bushes around us, covered with large flaps of meat, was to me, at this time, a novel sight; but it was one of those to which, in the following years, I became completely habituated; as the nature of the life we led rendered it a regular business.

'Within the colony, this animal is becoming daily more scarce; the boors, as well as the Hottentots, preferring its meat to that of any other antelope, and therefore, on every occasion, hunting it with the greatest eagerness. The principal cause of this preference, and at the same time, a very remarkable circumstance, is, its being the only one of the antelope genus, on which any considerable quantity of fat[6] is ever to be found; no other species yielding a hard fat from which candles may be made. . . . It is a practice, whenever it can be done, to drive their game as near home as possible, before it is shot; that they may not have to carry it far: but this cannot easily be done till, by a long chase, the animal begins to flag'.

Forty years later, eland were evidently becoming even more scarce: 'The eland is too bulky to run far; and, if pressed down wind by the horseman, his nostrils become so clogged with foam, that in ten minutes a very moderate nag compels him to stand still, panting, and awaiting the thrust of the knife, which is often used by the Boërs on such occasions. Hence, the eland is now very rarely found in the colony, as all have been killed, except perhaps a very few in the Winterfelt. Beyond the Orange River, in certain localities, this antelope is often found in small numbers, and, on account of the delicacy of his flesh, is hunted with avidity'. So wrote George Nicholson jr. in 1848, adding: 'But, after all, it is to the Eastern province, and beyond the Orange River, that the true sportsman will repair. Nowhere within the colonial boundary will a very great quantity of game be found, till the range of mountains called the Nieufeldt, the Winterbergen, and the Sneeuwbergen—different portions of the same chain—be passed. All the large herds of quaggas, gnoos, and springbucks, which Le Vaillant and other writers mention as having seen to the south of these mountains, are now scattered and dispersed by the incessant pursuit of which they have for so many years been the object; but, having emerged from the hills, and entered the boundless plains beyond, the accusation of exaggeration which has assailed the accounts of all those who have attempted to describe the living masses of wild animals seen, is at once acknowledged to have been unjust, and

[6]It is on account of this, and the excellence of its meat that, today, attention is being given to the possibility of domesticating the eland. J. L. C-T.

gives place to wonder and delight, as one contemplates the free and graceful movements of these wild herds in their own clime, and associated with the strange scenery of these regions'.

Lions were not uncommon near Cape Town as late as 1707. By 1842, however, the last lion south of the Orange River had been killed: in 1865 the last lion was shot in Natal. In 1848, Nicholson also wrote: 'A very few years ago, great numbers of them were to be found in the Boutebok "flats", at no great distance from Graham's Town, but the zeal and skill of some rare Nimrods in the regiments stationed on the Eastern frontier have notably diminished them'. He went on to describe how lions were approached by a party on horseback who then dismounted and fired from behind a rampart formed by backing their horses towards them, adding: 'The horses often suffer if the first volley poured in is not successful; but, not infrequently, the hunters have been either killed, wounded, or desperately frightened on such occasions'.

In the second volume of his *Travels*, published in 1824, W. J. Burchell wrote that as early as 1812 the rhinoceros had been almost expelled from Cape Colony; 'it being very rarely to be seen within the boundary: and hippopotami, formerly so numerous in the Zeekoe river, are no longer, unless accidentally, to be found there; but have all retreated to the Black River or Nagariep, where they may, for the present at least, live more undisturbed'. On the other hand, he mentioned that game was still plentiful in the region south of the Kalahari: 'The forests or groves of those countries, as far as hitherto explored, are known to abound in elephants. Their tusks are collected by the natives, partly for their own use in making ivory rings and other ornaments, and partly for barter with a few Hottentots who occasionally visit them for that purpose; but it is yet to be ascertained, whether the whole of the ivory thus collected by the Bachapins finds its way into the Colony. . . .'.

Game was common in the region of Tunobis in the Kalahari Desert about one hundred years ago, for Charles Andersson (1856) wrote: 'From the absence of water within a distance of two or three days' journey of the place, the number of animals that nightly congregated here to quench their thirst, was truly astonishing. To give the reader an idea of the immense quantity of game hereabouts, I may mention, that in the course of the few days we remained at Tunobis, our party shot, amongst other animals, upwards of thirty rhinoceroses. One night, indeed, when quite alone, I killed in the space of five hours (independently of other game) no less than eight of these beasts, amongst which were three distinct species.[7] And it is my belief that if I had persevered I might have destroyed double the number'. Again,

[7]Not so. J. L. C-T.

to be fair, it should be added that Andersson claimed that he did not delight in useless slaughter and that not a pound of flesh was ever wasted, for what was not required by his party was devoured by the local population. Even so, it is difficult to imagine the slaughter of thirty rhinos with equanimity.

Except for a few springbucks and several other kinds of antelope such as the grysbock, steenbok, duiker and here and there a few scattered oribi, the endless flats and kopjes of the Karoo have now little to show of the teeming life that swarmed over them only a short while ago. When Jan van Riebeeck landed at the Cape in 1652, eland were to be found on Table Mountain and the quagga existed in herds of countless thousands. By 1840 eland had almost been shot out of Cape Colony and today there are few of them left anywhere in South Africa apart from the Kalahari region and South-West Africa. Quaggas were slaughtered in such vast numbers to feed native workers and for their hides that few survived even until the second half of the last century. A few years later, Burchell's zebra suffered the same fate.[8]

Captain C. S. R. Pitman gives this graphic picture of the decline in numbers of South African wildlife: 'By 1871 the magnificent Kudu had become very rare in Cape Colony. Hide hunters exterminated the Black Wildebeest which still survives in captivity—and reduced the Blue Wildebeest, which once numbered hundreds of thousands, well-nigh to vanishing point. The Cape Hartebeest, abundant in 1652 is now extinct. The strange-looking Bontebok, formerly abundant in Cape Colony, has been reduced to a few herds which are preserved in a National Park, as well as on a few farms. As far back as 1836, owing to its scarcity, it was specially protected by the Cape Government. The closely allied Blesbok now occurs only in a Game Reserve in the Orange Free State and on some private property; during the 1863-83 period, hide hunters massacred it in tens of thousands and it was exterminated in many localities. Both the lovely Sable Antelope and the equine Roan Antelope are now extinct in much of South Africa, where once plentiful.

'In 1900, the Blaaubok or Blue Roan of the Cape had been extinct for just over a century. The handsome Gemsbok no longer occurs in the karoos of the Cape Province where once abundant, and where it was still numerous in 1844. The Springbok used to occur on the High Veld in millions, but in the Union it now exists, in some thousands only, mainly on fenced farms. It is still found in considerable numbers in the Kalahari region. The "treks", or migrations, of the old days were of such inconceivable magnitude as to constitute a major disaster in a settled area for the region traversed was rendered useless for

Street, 1961.

stock. Gone are the great herd of Elephant, and gone too is the spectacle of plains dotted with numerous grazing White and browsing Black Rhinoceroses. The Hippopotamus is another species which long ago disappeared from localities in which it was once common'.

So much for the eastern part of South Africa, where irreparable damage was done long before wild life and settlement came into real conflict. In East Africa the situation is somewhat different as the country was opened up so much more recently. But first let us consider the northern part of the continent.

North Africa and the Nile Valley

Although much of the Sahara has long been arid, game was fairly plentiful in favourable localities even until comparatively recent times. Two thousand years ago, elephants lived among the forests on the foothills of the Atlas Mountains and Hanno saw them on the shores of the Atlantic about 500 B.C. Lions too, were widely distributed until the coming of fire-arms : they were common in Algeria, for example, until the time of the French occupation of that country. By the middle of the last century, however, their numbers had been greatly diminished. This decrease was largely due to the high price placed on their heads by the Turkish Government in the Barbary States : a policy continued on a smaller scale by the French. Before then, there were many lions in the forest-clad hills and mountains of Algeria, Tunisia and other North African countries.[9]

Cheetahs were plentiful too and at one time were caught and trained for coursing game. Today there are no hunting cheetahs left and no wild ones except, possibly, a very few in the Tripolitanian desert of north-western Libya.

Various closely related varieties of gazelle have long been the main game animals of the Sahara. Now they are almost the only game left and are fast disappearing in their turn as military and oil company personnel, looking for fresh meat, accept any excuse to fire their guns. Occasional antelopes and mouflon were to be found in the region of the Mzab as recently as 70 years ago, but the former have now disappeared from all but a few corners of the northern central Sahara and the extreme southern edge of the desert. The latter have been reduced to a few scattered families in the central mountain massifs.

Ostriches were once numerous and used to be hunted extensively as far north as Laghourt. The last of the great western flocks were, however, exterminated a century ago by a series of organised hunts in which General Jean Margueritte, of Mexican fame, was the leading figure. In the north and eastern central desert, the chief agents of destruction were Tuareg bands of commercial hunters in search of

[9]Pease, 1913.

feathers. But here the work of destruction was not complete until the early years of the present century.[10]

The disappearance of game in recent years from the northern part of eastern Africa is clearly seen when we read the accounts of travellers voyaging down the Nile. 'In former times crocodiles flourished in that section of the Nile which flows through Lower Egypt. The crocodile was worshipped in Egypt from very early times as the representative of the Nile-god Sebek. The chief shrines were at Crocodilopolis in Upper Egypt: the people who dwelt near Thebes and the lake of Moeris regarded them as especially sacred. The people in each of these districts brought up one crocodile in particular. When this had been tamed, they placed, according to Herodotus, bracelets round its fore-feet. When these sacred reptiles died they were mummified. In other parts of Egypt crocodiles were hunted and killed as noxious beasts'.[11]

Crocodiles are now extremely scarce throughout Egypt but in 1816, Thomas Legh wrote as follows: 'In the course of this day [2 Feb. 1813], we passed Diospolis Parva, the modern How. It was a little before our arrival at this place, that we saw crocodiles for the first time; they were basking on the sand banks in the river, and some of the largest might be twenty-five feet long. I believe Girgeh may be considered the limit below which crocodiles do not descend; from this place to the Cataracts we observed them in great numbers; above Essouan, the sand banks in the Nile are less frequent, and, consequently fewer of these animals were to be seen. The superstitious natives attribute the circumstance of crocodiles not being observed in the lower parts of the Nile to the influence of a talisman fixed in the walls of the Mekkias, or Nilometer, at Cairo'.

Although rainfall and climatic conditions have probably not altered greatly since the Pleistocene (p. 2)[12], there is evidence that, until recently, the fauna in the central part of the Nile valley was comparatively rich. Thus an ivory tablet engraved with a drawing of a rhinoceros and other representations of elephants and giraffes have been found at Kerma, in Dongola district, where an Egyptian trading station was established about 1900 B.C. Diodorus (1st Century B.C.) described a tribe of elephant-eaters living in regions covered with thickets of trees growing close together, probably on the upper reaches of the Atbara river, and Strabo (c. 63 B.C.-A.D. 23) mentioned a hunting ground for elephants at Ptolemais near the modern Aqiq (p. 141).

About A.D. 60, the emperor Nero sent two centurians on an

[10]Briggs, 1960.
[11]Bland-Sutton, 1911.
[12]Jackson, J. K. (1957) *Sudan Notes Rec.* **38**, 47-65.

attempt to discover the source of the Nile. According to Pliny (A.D. 23-79) they found the tracks of elephants and rhinos around Merowe — 'Herbas circa Meroen demum viridiores silvarumque aliquid apparusse et rhinocerotum elephantorumque vestigia'. Certainly elephants could easily have lived near the Nile there, if the country were thinly populated and a certain amount of grass or marsh remained by the river; while rhinoceroses can withstand very dry conditions. During the 12th Century A.D., the Arab traveller Idrisi found elephants and giraffes near Dongola. According to Professor F. E. Zeuner (1963) the Egyptians of the late Gerzean period were familiar with elephants which probably became extinct in Egypt proper in early dynastic times.

In the journal of his journey up the Nile to Merowe in the years 1821 and 1822, Linant de Bellefonds (1958) commented on the animals and vegetation of the northern Sudan. The apparent woodedness of the countryside seems almost unbelievable to those who know the land today, whilst any report of a lion roaring near Ed Debba, near Old Dongola, would nowadays be regarded as a figment of the wildest imagination. Yet on 9 May 1822 Linant wrote: 'A minuit nous partimes de Dabba et passames peu après pas un bois très serré et plain d'épines, de sorte que malgré le clair de lune il fallait prendre bien des précautions pour ne pas nous aveugler et nos habits furent fort maltraités. Nous entendimes les rugissements d'un lion; mais il ne nous approcha pas. Il y en a dans ces bois et ils font souvent beaucoup de ravages dans les troupeaux des Arabes'.

G. A. Hoskins (1835) mentioned lions as being plentiful near Shendi 120 miles north of Khartoum. 'Every place and country has its danger, but few spread more alarm than this terror of the deserts. . . . By simply keeping up a few fires, the merchants who pass these deserts sleep securely, in defiance of their being infested by the most formidable of all wild beasts. I should, however, state, that instances are mentioned of fires not having this effect, when the lions are excessively pressed by hunger, particularly at the season when they require food for their young. Towards evening (for it is very seldom if ever, that the lion is seen during the day), one alone has often arrested a large caravan. In some instances they have been known to attack men; but are generally content with an ox or a camel, which they kill, and sometimes, particularly if they have left their female or young in their den, carry away a large part on their shoulders. The number of these animals must increase rapidly every year, for it is very seldom that an instance occurs of one being killed. . . . They infest the road to Sennaar and the west side of the Atbara; but travellers incur less danger in the beaten track of the caravans than when, like us, they deviate from it'.

He also said that he saw on the road 'numerous traces of the lions, hyenas, tigres (nimr), wild asses, and ostriches, and near the river, guinea-fowls' and that he 'could have bought for four shillings the skin of a giraffe. This animal, only so recently known in Europe, is found in great numbers on the road from Debba to Kordofan, between Sabrian and Gibel el Arazi, and behind Kordofan, on the Bahr el Abiad, the territory of the Buggara tribe'.

J. H. Churi wrote in 1853 that: 'The hippopotamus begins to be seen from Atbara up, and Atbara itself possesses a few of them. . . . It is the most powerful animal in the Nile, and even the ferocious and horrible crocodile fears it. It feeds upon grass and vegetables, which it seeks amongst the banks or isles at its leisure. . . .'. He described the following scene on the Nile near Berber a year earlier: 'Not far from us, was a hippopotamus swimming, and opposite on a little island lay two others; but the finest sight was a crocodile stretched in the sun, on an island, on the Eastern side, although very near the bank where the men were with oxen turning a wheel for drawing water, it appeared to despise them; for more than half an hour we gazed on, as it lay motionless like a long great pine; taking our spy-glasses, we saw its den of a mouth, and its sharp white teeth like bayonets. It was surrounded by a troop of birds, and certainly could not be less than thirty-five or forty feet long, its sight at a distance was frightful, the enormous head was enough to frighten anyone. . . .'.

John Petherick (1861) described the land on either side of the Nile only as far south of Khartoum as the Abba island in the following words: 'The occupants of this imposing wild were herds of antelopes and gazelles; and in the morning, a veteran lion or a female with her cubs, on our approach, would slink from the confines of the stream into the underwood. Small blue monkeys bounded from tree to tree, and now and then raced playfully along the open beach. The stream was wide, and the lowness of its banks admitted the floods far into the interior of the bush. No trace of man was visible'. He and his wife (1869) also saw hippopotamuses north of Berber, near Atbara.

Again, F. L. James (1883) recorded an abundance of game at Cassala (Kassala). Although his engraving of the Gebel (Jebel) shows a landscape as arid as it is today, 'The natives told us that a lion prowled about Fillik, and had killed several people. . . . Guinea-fowl were plentiful, and there were many kinds of bright-plumaged birds . . . plenty of gazelles; and we saw for the first time the beautiful Dorcas gazelle. . . .'. Only three days' march from Kassala he saw the fresh tracks of elephants, which he followed; they took him to the Gash, where he found a good deal of water on the surface where the bed was rocky and narrower than he had previously seen it.

A few years earlier, however, game had begun to be scarce along the Nile in the northern Sudan. A. S. Southwood (1875) searched in vain for crocodiles and hippopotamuses between Abu Hamed and Berber in the northern Sudan. He wrote: 'Curiously enough, the race of elephants have been pushing southward each year, chased by the ivory traders, wars and civilisation. The traders from Zanzibar have likewise driven the monsters into the interior, and it is thought that a few years more will suffice to extinguish the last vestige of the African colossi. They are no more at the Bahr el-Ghazal, but are now hovering near the equator. I tried to discover how many of the beasts exist—that is, the elephantine population—and, as near as I can estimate, there remain in Central Africa 100,000, more or less. It is but a few years ago that elephants were found as high as the fourteenth degree of north latitude'.

In 1900 E. S. Grogan and A. H. Sharp described the fauna on the banks of the Nile near Bor as follows: 'Owing to the absence of water and quantity of plum-trees of which they are very fond, there were enormous numbers of elephant along the river-bank, and except where they were on the path we scarcely noticed them, every day passing several herds. . . . The numbers of hippos were incredible, literally thousands and thousands. At every two hundred yards there was a great purple bank of twenty, fifty, or a hundred lying with their bodies half exposed, while others were wandering about in every direction on the vegetation, islands, and mud-banks. They practically ignored our presence, though we often passed within ten yards of them. Other game was scarce; I only saw a few waterbuck, bushbuck, and once the track of a giraffe'.

The great Bor elephant herd still exists but hippopotamuses are less numerous and scarcely occur north of the sudd. Yet as recently as 1924, according to J. G. Millais, there were still 'a good many hippopotami in this part of the Nile [near Kosti], and we saw our first little herd of them one morning, blowing and snorting under the lee of a small island. They were very shy, but other herds, which we encountered almost every day, were fairly tame and watched us at close range putting up their black heads with little piggy eyes'.

Writing in 1911, J. Bland-Sutton claimed that the traffic on the Lower Nile, the persecutions to which they are subject from modern fire-arms, as well as the turmoil caused by paddle-boats and stern-wheelers, had driven the crocodile almost completely out of the Nile below Khartoum.

As a footnote it is a pleasure to add that we still get crocodiles occasionally at Khartoum and, in 1961, my servant brought me some crocodile eggs from his village near Dongola. If they were given a fair chance I am sure these fine reptiles could soon re-establish themselves throughout much of the Nile.

Central eastern Africa

The situation regarding the game in Central eastern Africa is somewhat less depressing than it is further north and south, largely because European penetration of the area has been so much more recent. When the white man first came, wild life was certainly far more abundant and widespread than it is today but, fortunately, there has not yet been enough time to reap such extensive havoc as has taken place in South Africa.

Before the whites came, there was no poverty in eastern Africa. The population was approximately static, adjusted by tribal customs and a high infantile mortality rate. Hunting was strictly organised territorially and effective close seasons, coinciding with antelopes' breeding times, were rigidly enforced. Some non-hunting tribes occasionally also ate meat, but their spasmodic individual forays against the wild animals did little harm, whilst the nomadic pastoralists ate no meat at all. 'Another factor which helped to preserve individual species is the totem system whereby a certain animal is sacred to a tribe or section thereof, and therefore cannot be molested. So long as animals were killed solely for human needs, i.e. for meat, skins, etc., and not for commercial gain there was no cause for apprehension. But, of course, the principal safeguard the game had at that time was the fact that rarely was a tribe at peace with its neighbours, and in consequence everywhere there were considerable areas of "no man's land" which the respective tribes found wisest to avoid'.[13]

Ethiopia was one of the first countries in this part of Africa to be visited by Europeans. Of its fauna, James Bruce wrote in 1790: 'Among the wild animals are prodigious numbers of the gazel, or antelope kind; the bohur, fassa, feeko, and madoque, and various others; these are seldom found in the cultivated country, or where cattle pasture, as they chiefly feed on trees; for the most part, they are found in broken ground near the banks of rivers, where, during the heat of the day, they conceal themselves, and sleep under cover of the bushes; they are still more numerous in those provinces whose inhabitants have been extirpated, and the houses ruined or burnt in time of war, and where wild oats, grown up so as to cover the whole country, afford them a quiet residence, without being disturbed by man'.

'The elephant, rhinoceros, giraffa, or camelopardalis, are inhabitants of the low hot country; nor is the lion, or leopard, faadh, which is the panther, seen in the high and cultivated country. There are no tigers in Abyssinia, nor, as far as I know, in Africa; it is an Asiatic animal; for what reason some travellers, or naturalists, have called him the

[13]C. R. S. Pitman *loc. cit.*

tiger-wolf, or mistaken him altogether for the tiger, is what I cannot discover. Innumerable flocks of apes, and baboons of different kinds, destroy the fields of millet everywhere. . . .'.

At about the same period, W. G. Browne[14] (1799) gave the following account of wild life in Darfur, western Sudan: 'The wild or ferocious animals are, principally the lion, the leopard, the hyena (Fûr. murfaên, dubba, Ar.) the wolf, the jackal, Canis aureus, the wild buffaloe: but they are not commonly seen within the more cultivated part of the empire, at least that which I have visited, excepting the hyena and the jackal; the former come in herds of six, eight, and often more, into all the villages at night, and carry off with them whatever they are able to master. They will kill dogs, and asses, even within the enclosure of the houses, and fail not to assemble wherever a dead camel or other animal is thrown, which, acting in concert, they sometimes drag to a prodigious distance; nor are they greatly alarmed at the sight of a man or the report of fire-arms, which I have often discharged at them, and occasionally with effect. It is related that upon one of them being wounded, his companions instantly tear him to pieces and devour him; but I have had no opportunity of ascertaining this fact. . . .'.

'In the countries bordering on the empire of Fûr, where water is in greater abundance, the other animals mentioned are very numerous, and much dreaded by travellers, particularly on the banks of the Bahr-el-Ada. To those already enumerated, may be added, the elephant, the rhinoceros, the camelopardalis, the hippopotamus, and the crocodile. The elephant is seen, in the places he frequents, in large herds of four or five hundred, according to report. It is even said that two thousand are sometimes found together; but I do not suspect the Arabs of extreme accuracy in counting. . . . His hide is applied to many useful purposes. The African elephant is smaller than the Asiatic[15], and probably of a different species. The meat is an article of food in great esteem with them. The fat forms a valuable unguent, and the teeth, as is well known, supply the merchants with immense profits'.

'The buffaloe is not found tame in Soudân. The wild one is hunted by the Arabs, and serves them for food. The hippopotamus is killed for his skin (which is remarkably tough, makes excellent shields and whips not wholly unlike our horse-whips); and for his teeth, which are much superior to ivory. The horn of the rhinoceros, to which animal the Arabs have applied a term somewhat less appropriate than the Greek, but still characteristic, (Abu-kurn, father of the one horn),

[14]Later murdered in Teheran at the age of 45 on his way to Tartary.
[15]See p. 141.

makes a valuable article of trade, and is carried to Egypt, where it is sold at an high price, being used for sabre-hilts, and various other purposes. The more credulous attribute to it some efficacy as an antidote against poison. The antelope and the ostrich are extremely common throughout the empire. The civet-cat is not seen wild in the quarter which I visited, but is frequent enough farther to the South. Many are preferred in cages in the houses of the rich. The women apply the odour extracted from them to add to their personal allurements; and what is not thus disposed of becomes an article of trade.

'The lion and leopard, though common in a certain district are not found near the seat of government. The Arabs hunt them, strip off the skin, which they sell, and often eat the flesh, which they conceive generates courage and a warlike disposition. They occasionally take them young, and bring them for sale to the Jelabs, who sometimes carry them as presents to the great men in Egypt'.

Half a century later, we read that: 'The hippopotamus is found in the Taccazy, but I believe nowhere else in Tigrè. The lake Tzana and other waters of the Amhara country are plentifully stocked with the animal: there is a tribe called "Commaunt" that subsists entirely on fish and the flesh of the hippopotamus; the hide is used for making whips'.[16] This indicates a nice balance between the hippo and its human predators.

The Ethiopian fauna was still apparently extremely rich even in 1877 when E. A. de Cosson wrote: 'In the low wooded valleys by the rivers, elephants, hippopotami, rhinoceri, lions, leopards, panthers, buffalos—in short, most of the larger animals indigenous to Central Africa are to be met with; while there are endless varieties of gazelle and antelope kind on the higher plains. . . . The ivory, though of excellent quality is never very large'.

Turning now to East Africa; a century ago, Sir Richard Burton (1860) said of the fauna of the lake regions of Central Africa: 'In the jungles quadrumana are numerous; lions and leopards, cynhyaenas and wild cats haunt the forests; the elephant and the rhinoceros, the giraffe and the Cape buffalo, the zebra, the quagga (?),[17] and the koodoo wander over the plains; and the hippopotamus and crocodile are found in every large pool'.

'Wild animals abound through these jungles, and the spoor lasts long upon the crisp gravelly soil. In some districts they visit by night the raised clay water-troughs of the cultivators. The elephant prefers the thick jungle, where he can wallow in the pools and feed delicately upon succulent roots and fruits, bark, and leaves. The rhinoceros loves the dark clumps of trees, which guard him from the noonday sun,

[16]Parkyns, 1853.
[17]The question mark is Burton's.

and whence he can sally out all unexpected upon the assailant. The mbogo, or Bos Caffer, driven from his favourite spots, low grassy plains bordering on streams, wanders, like the giraffe, through the thinner forests. As in Unyamwezi, the roar of the lion strikes the ear by night, and the cry of the ostrich by day'.

Five years later, David and Charles Livingstone wrote as follows about the game around latitude 16°31'S.: 'A short way beyond the Ruo lies the elephant marsh, or Nyanja Mukulu, which is frequented by vast herds of these animals. We believe that we counted eight hundred elephants in sight at once. In the choice of such a stronghold, they have shown their usual sagacity, for no hunter can get near them through the swamps. . . . In passing the Elephant Marsh, we saw nine large herds of elephants; they sometimes formed a line two miles long'.

Now a quotation from Speke's Journal for 13 August 1858 when he was on his way to Lake Tanganyika: 'Travelling through the Nindo Wilderness today, the Beluches were very much excited at the quantity of game they saw; but though they tried their best, they did not succeed in killing any. Troops of zebras, and giraffe, some varieties of antelopes roaming about in large herds, a buffalo and one ostrich, were the chief visible tenants of this wild. We saw the fresh prints of a very large elephant. . . .'.

Next, in 1872, H. M. Stanley said of the country just east of Lake Tanganyika: 'I was able to shoot several animals during our stay at Mrera. The forest outside of the cultivation teems with noble animals. Zebra, giraffe, elephant, and rhinoceros are most common: ptarmigan and guinea-fowl were also plentiful'.

On 13 August 1874, Frank Oates (1881), on his third attempt to reach the Zambesi, wrote in his journal: 'Today, soon after starting I ascended a kopje near the waggons, and saw a large herd of quagga [zebra]. Counting roughly, I made out a hundred. It was a beautiful sight. All around was the sea of bush, with here and there bare patches, and here and there kopjes, some of the latter far distant. . . . The quaggas were quietly moving on, or standing and playing, or brushing away the flies. It was a scene such as I used to fancy must be common, and probably was so when the accounts I have read were written, and may occur often still in more remote districts'.

J. F. Elton (1879), H.M. Consul at Mozambique, recorded an immense herd of over 300 elephant—some of them bathing, others sleeping in the grass or wallowing in the marsh—at the north end of Lake Nyassa in October, 1877. Constantly throughout his journals one comes upon references to large herds of game animal, hippopotamuses, crocodiles and so on.

When Joseph Thomson (1885) arrived in Tanganyika he too was still able to see plenty of game. His description well conveys the

excitement and splendour of the sight: 'There', he wrote, 'towards
the base of Kilimanjaro, are three great herds of buffalo slowly and
leisurely moving up from the lower grazing grounds to the shelter of
the forest for their daily snooze and rumination in its gloomy depths.
Farther out on the plains enormous numbers of the harmless but
fierce-looking wildebeest continue their grazing, some erratic members
of the herd gambolling and galloping about, with waving tail and
strange uncouth movements. Mixed with these are to be seen companies of that loveliest of all large game, the zebra, conspicuous in
their beautiful striped skin—here marching with stately step, with
heads bent down, there enjoying themselves by kicking their heels
in mid-air or running open-mouthed in mimic flight, anon standing
as if transfixed, with heads erect and projecting ears, watching the
caravan pass. But these are not all. Look ! Down in that grassy bottom
there are several specimens of the great, unwieldy rhinoceros, with
horns stuck on their noses in a most offensive and pugnacious manner.
Over that ridge a troop of ostriches are scudding away out of reach of
danger, defying pursuit, and too wary for the stalker. See how
numerous are the herds of hartebeest; and notice the graceful pallah
(impala) springing into mid-air with great bounds, as if in pure enjoyment of existence. There also, among the tall reeds near the marsh,
you perceive the dignified waterbuck, in twos and threes, leisurely
cropping the dewy grass. The warthog, disturbed at his morning's
feast, clears off in a bee-line with tail erect, and with a steady military
trot, truly comical. These do not exhaust the list, for there are many
other species of game. Turn in whatever direction you please, they
are to be seen in astonishing numbers, and so rarely hunted, that
unconcernedly they stand and stare at us, within gunshot'.

The situation had not yet begun to deteriorate further inland at
the edge of the Congo, for T. H. Parke wrote in his diary for 23 July
1887: 'There are several villages on the opposite bank of the
Aruwimi; there are also plenty of bananas there but none on this
side. There appears, however, to be plenty of game: judging from the
footprints, I should say that there are thousands of elephants in our
vicinity; but it is absolutely impossible to shoot anything as the forest
is so dense'.

The following entry, a week later, shows that the impact of commercial hunting had not yet reached that part of the country: 'We
found twelve elephants' tusks (about the value of £400) lying uncared
for about this village. They are used by the natives as seats; they do
not know the great commercial value of ivory, for no traders have
ever penetrated so far into the forest'.

Between the years 1853-1879, however, some 3,706 tons of ivory
were exported from the Sudan through Suakin, most of it destined

for India and the East, according to Denman (1957) and even greater quantities for Zanzibar, and elsewhere. It is therefore not surprising that by 1881, Frederick Courtenay Selous (1893) had already spent ten years of his life 'elephant hunting in the interior, and every year elephants were becoming scarcer and wilder south of the Zambesi, so that it had become almost impossible to make a living by hunting at all'.

Writing in *The Field* in 1908, Selous said much the same of buffalo: 'Throughout the whole of that part of Africa south of the Zambesi there are now but very few buffaloes, comparatively speaking, left alive. In this part of the continent these fine animals have entirely ceased to exist over vast areas throughout which they once ranged in great numbers'. This was due to rinderpest (p. 84) as well as to shooting. He added that in many parts of tropical Africa elephants continued to exist in enormous numbers, but that big tuskers (over 75 lbs) were very much reduced in numbers. In 1902, almost every official in Uganda succeeded in shooting the two elephants allowed him on his licence each year, one or both of which frequently had tusks over 100 lbs in weight and tusks in the region of 150 lbs were not uncommon. By 1908 even, these were very scarce.

By 1886, the game north of the Limpopo River had long been exterminated as illustrated by the following quotation from Walter Montagu Kerr. 'While here I scoured the country for miles in search of game, but without any luck, although in bygone days there used to be an abundance of sport in these parts. That was before the war of extermination had been fairly started. Now, through the common property of gunpowder and the familiarity of arms to the natives, this region has been laid waste. You may travel not only for miles but for days in the veldt without seeing a living thing, save a few birds and, perhaps, a duiker. By no means a long time ago the shrill trumpeting of the elephant might be heard echoing among the kopjies which bank the river on the north; hundreds of giraffes browsed and found shelter in the luxuriant mopani forests; in short, almost every species of wild animal to be found in South Africa was common among the now silent groves which fringe the Inkwezi.

'The native hunters, with their rude-looking arms, have been the exterminators. The finely-finished, specially-made rifles of the keen white sportsman have done little harm among the big game, compared to the havoc made by these imperfect-looking weapons, with their clumsy sticks covered with hide, and altogether resembling a gas-pipe with a frozen clod of earth at one end'. This may have been special pleading, but it is true that in many parts Europeans have done even more harm to wild game by introducing fire-arms to Africans than by their own greedy hunting.

Conditions were better in the more inaccessible southern Sudan, and General C. G. Gordon (1881), en route for Gondokoro, wrote in his diary of March 1874, 'We saw a huge troop of wild buffaloes yesterday, looking as black as coals. They are the most ferocious animals, and by far the most dangerous to shoot of any wild animal.[18] ... We saw nine camelopards, two days ago eating the tops of trees; they looked like steeples. Very many hippopotamuses bellowing all night and fighting. . . . Crocodiles in abundance, and all sorts of strange birds'.

Shortly afterwards, Emin Pasha[19] [Eduard Schnitzer] (1888) recorded many instances of the plentifulness of game animals in Equatoria. One 'paradise of elephants is named by the Liria people Kadenokoka; the Latuka people call it Kittagong. . . . Kigalias and euphorbias grow on the elevated spots, while hundreds of elephants march about in troops, not exactly improving the road, which is so trodden down by them that one has the greatest difficulty in steering one's course unharmed between the holes and ditches'.

Again, 'elephants are to be found in great numbers in the woods of Kafu [Equatoria]; lions prowl round the cattle enclosures in couples, leopards and hyenas; besides jackals, crowds of antelopes, gazelles, and wild boars abound on the tablelands and valleys'—this from G. Casati (1891) who spent ten years in Equatoria Province, Sudan.

Further south, Sir Gerald Portal (1894) recorded that around Lake Naivasha 'the prairies were literally covered with game', especially Thomson's gazelle. 'Zebras, too, were present in fair numbers, though very wild, and a few hartebeest and Grant's antelope added to the variety. . . .'.

The game between Mombasa and Khuyu at this time has been described by G. F. Scott Elliot (1896) in the following words: 'Game is abundant everywhere, a kind of small bustard and guinea-fowl being very common. Occasionally a tiny gazelle, "paa", with large ears, springs out of the thorns and vanishes down the path. I saw footprints of giraffe, and came across ostriches more than once. . . . From Languru to the beginning of the Kikuyu bush is a very gradual ascent, and forms the well-known Athi plains. The abundance of game is still extraordinary, in spite of the amount of exterminations which has been practised by certain persons. A toll of 380 head in three months fell to one "sportsman", which, considering that a little antelope meat is a great blessing to the caravans on this road, seems quite inexcusable. A curious feature is the abundance of the *Kongoni*, or hartebeest, the most timid as well as the ugliest of them all. . . .'.

[18]See, however, p. 126, J. L. C-T.
[19]Governor of Equatoria province, Sudan, during the Mahdia: relieved by H. M. Stanley in the expedition of 1888.

From there to Lake Victoria: 'It gives a curious impression to march day after day over lovely grass plains covered with zebra, hartebeest, and other antelopes, past beautiful lakes where geese, ducks, and other water-fowl almost cover the water, then perhaps through a dense virgin forest with magnificent timber, and all the time to see no human beings whatever. Yet the country is healthy and in every way suited to Europeans, while we have hundreds of people in England who do not know where to turn for employment'.

Later, however, Scott Elliot wrote: 'Game in Karagwe is usually conspicuous by its absence. The most important animal is the rhinoceros ... as a rule these animals do not charge out of sheer wickedness. In this country, however, the natives appear sometimes to collect in large bands and spear them, and this may account for their timidity. ... Other game is very rare. I once saw a troop of zebras, and on two or three occasions we came across hartebeest.

'The number of elephants now existing in British territory is not by any means a large one. . . . They still exist not very far from Kikuyu to the north-east and apparently extend all round Kenia, and from there on to Mont Elgon. I came across numerous traces of them in the Mau forest, between Raomi and the Guaso Masai. There are also probably some left in Sotik and Lumbwa. From Elgon they appear to be found along the Somerset Nile to Unyoro and the Albert Nyanza (in Chagwe, occasionally, coming within four days' journey of Kampala). There appear to be plenty in the forest district around Kivari, between the Mpango river and Ruwenzori and, as I have mentioned, they are always to be found somewhere between Chukarongo and Kasagamas on the east side of the mountain. A few probably still exist in the Nyamgassa river, a little north of the Salt lake. There are also a few on the eastern shore of the Albert Edward Nyanza, north-west of Makowallis, and a little south-east of my route. This probably exhausts the localities for the East African sphere, unless some are still left on Kilimanjaro. In the German sphere of influence there may be some on Kilimanjaro, but they are probably completely absent now from Karagwe, Urandi, and the whole eastern shore of Tanganyika. The belt of papyrus (on the Kagera river) is about 80 yards wide on either side, and the water is, as usual, full of hippopotami. . . .'.

These comments certainly imply that the game in certain parts of Kenya was becoming more scarce towards the end of the last century. At the same time, I think that it may never have been very plentiful in some of the places visited by Scott Elliot, who mistakenly blamed its scarcity on the activities of hunters. It is sometimes difficult to assess the changes that have taken place because, naturally enough, travellers tend to remark more on the presence than on the absence of game.

However, the fact that during the 1890s, hunters in Rhodesia were all mounted on proven horses indicates that conditions were different there in those days. According to Marcus Daly (1937), 'elephant, buffalo and lion were alike seen moving in the open by day. Later, in defence, the elephant kept to the thick country, and moved further north into the tsetse-fly country, where horses had to be given up as the best of them lived only a few months'. Thus at one time tsetse afforded protection to game but later, as we shall see, they became an excuse for game extermination.

In Nyasaland, hippo on the Shire river were reduced in numbers because they were said to be a menace to canoes (p. 116). On the Zambesi they were potted by everyone and often only wounded. Then it was the turn of the elephant. E. Foá, in 1894, found that there was hardly any game near Cheramo. He wrote (1899): 'In the Zambesi country, I have never killed an elephant which had not several native bullets in its body, or did not bear traces of ancient or recent wounds'. Conditions such as this cannot long be tolerated by wild life.

Around 1906, however, according to A. B. Lloyd, there were innumerable crocodiles in the Victoria Nile near Murchison Falls. 'It is a most enchanting place; looking down from the top of the hill right into the Nile one could count hundreds of crocodiles' snouts jutting out of the water, and on a sand bank just across the river there were thirty or forty of these monstrous reptiles asleep, some with their huge jaws wide open and others looking more like logs of wood stretched out in the heat of the sun. . . . To the west, not more than 200 yards away, I counted twenty-odd hippos, some of them right out of the water, others with just their noses showing. . . .'.

Surely these words could have been written yesterday. On the other hand, large prides of lions no longer occurred as before. During the mid-19th century, lions and elephants were almost exterminated on the coast of Somaliland by officers of the Indian Army and Aden Government some of whom could boast of killing five lions before breakfast. A. E. Pease (1913) estimated that 1,000 lions were shot in 12 years and he himself noticed over 60 between December 1896 and March 1897. He recorded that his friend, H. Chalmer, had seen 15 lions in one troop near Embu in 1909 and that his tent boy, who was no liar, saw 28 together one day in Somaliland. The Hon. Galbraith Cole told him that he was once passing through a number of kongoni hartebeest when he suddenly realised that one particular group was not kongoni at all, but lions, and he counted 23-25 of them all around him.

In the year 1906, Sir Richard Dane marched from Naivasha to the Aberdare mountains in Kenya. In his book *Sport in Asia and Africa*

Hippopotamus
mother and child,
Murchison Nile,
Uganda

Male lion, Kenya

Leopard, Seronera, Tanzania

Buffalo wallow, Uganda

(1921) he wrote that rhinoceroses were still fairly numerous though they did not appear to carry good horns.

A region, both inaccessible and naturally rich in game, was Gambela on the Sudan-Ethiopian border east of the sudd. According to A. Henry Savage Landor (1907) who travelled 8,500 miles across the widest part of Africa in 364 days: 'There are innumerable crocodiles in the stream and many hippopotami, while the banks are lined with birds of valuable plumage. We were here in a country extraordinarily rich in game—elephants, giraffes, lions, leopards, ostriches, hyaenas and antelopes being quite plentiful. We marched over a wide, treeless, flat country, so trampled upon by elephants in the wet season that thousands of deep holes — their footmarks — covered the whole country, and were a great nuisance—in fact, quite a danger—for my animals'.

Wild game was also plentiful near the frontier between Bahr el-Ghazal and French Congo and 'we saw some large buck, two wart-hogs and several giraffes. In fact, I was nearly knocked down by a giraffe in flight as I was trying to photograph it only five or six yards away. We heard the trumpeting of elephants during the night, and we saw some in the afternoon crashing a passage through the forest. They were frightened of something and were stampeding. I do not know that I have ever seen such an impressive sight. A dozen or so of these brutes forced their way through the forest. The disturbance they made, bellowing and smashing everything along the passage, was deafening. They passed only a short distance from us'.

Near Mongalla in the southern Sudan, Edward Fothergill (1910) was called by one of the sailors of the river steamer in which he was travelling to see a sight that he would not have missed for the world. 'We had just rounded one of the numerous sharp curves in the river, and had just come suddenly upon a gigantic herd of elephant which had been drinking and playing about the banks. The herd included numerous baby elephants and I was awakened in time to see them at play before they became aware of our approach. It was one of the prettiest sights which I have ever seen. Most of the baby elephants were right on the banks of the river, or had waded some way out into the water for a bathe. Their mothers were plastering them with mud, and then washing it off with copious spouts of water from their trunks. At the very lowest computation there must have been quite four hundred animals in the herd. As soon as they became conscious of the presence of the steamer, they beat a dignified retreat into the surrounding jungles; there was no hurry; they simply strolled off, some of them picking green shoots off the trees as they went'.

In the same year, R. C. F. Maugham wrote as follows: 'The wide plains and forests bordering upon the Zambezi River are still the

permanent abiding places of large quantities of wild animals. . . .
Elephant, rhinoceros . . . zebras, and buffaloes are still found in fair
quantities, and the sobby grunt of the amorous hippopotamus is heard
on all the streams and marshes throughout the country'. Lion and
leopard 'are sufficiently numerous to be a source of considerable
danger and loss of life among the native races, Europeans at times
falling victims to them as well. As I have just stated, Elephants are
not uncommon. They must have existed a few decades ago in considerable numbers, but as the original primitive means of transport
on the river gave place to steamer, and more and more settlers began
to arrive, the great herds were either killed off by native hunters in
the employ of Europeans or wandered farther away from the settlements to localities where it no longer paid to follow them. The
"gigantic rain-puddle", as Moore calls the Victoria Nyanza, swarms
with crocodiles, and they lie sunning themselves on the rocks or
concealed in the water waiting for antelopes, men, women, and
children. . . . In Murchison Bay there is a small conical islet (Kabula-
taka) thickly covered with trees. When the Mahomedan party was
defeated, Mutesa ordered the prisoners to be placed on this island and
left there to die of starvation or to be eaten by the crocodiles which
haunted its margins. A military guard on the mainland prevented the
prisoners from swimming ashore. None escaped'.[20]

Major E. M. Jack (1914) wrote of Ruanda: 'The country is delight-
fully open, and easy to traverse; the grass is quite short, and gentle,
rounded hills alternate with broad, open valleys. All over these rolling
downs there are quantities of game. The commonest antelope are the
topi, which are found in immense herds, frequently, according to their
custom, in company with their friends the zebra. There are also large
herds of impala, one of the most graceful of antelopes, with beautiful
slender, lyre-shaped horns. Eland and roan are found in small
numbers. . . . Oribi we saw everywhere. These little creatures always
seem to go about in pairs, and when they run away they continually
take enormous leaps into the air. . . . The little mouse-coloured duiker
would often spring up from under our feet and dash off in the grass,
and reedbuck, with which we had been well acquainted in Uganda,
were commonly seen. Hyaenas and jackals were pretty numerous, as
was also the king of beasts, the lion, who found in this country an
inexhaustible larder. His favourite food seemed to be the zebra'.

In 1927, C. W. Domville Fife described the fauna of Imatong
Mountains on the Sudan-Uganda border in the following words: 'The
country is covered with heavy undergrowth as well as with patches
of dense equatorial forest. The range, which forms an imposing back-
ground, varies in altitude from 5000 to 7000 feet. The scenery is most

[20]Bland-Sutton, 1919.

picturesque and the whole region abounds in big game. Lions, elephants, buffaloes and antelopes are to be seen almost every day while on *safari*, and these beasts have not yet become gun-shy'.

Between the wars there was evidently plenty of game in the central part of eastern Africa despite the slaughter that continued. Although commercial hunting was reduced and game reserves established, poaching increased in proportion as we shall see.

Mrs. P. Ness (1929) recalled that there were many lions and leopards around the neighbourhood of Torit (southern Sudan), but added: 'There may have been much wild life in the forest, but only once did we see a buck, which leapt exhausted into the road and staggered across, the car missing it by only a few feet. . . . Behind the tired gazelle followed a lion that recoiled at the glare of the head-lights'.

In his book . . . *something new out of Africa* (1934) H. W. also wrote of the Sudan 'While in the south recently I heard of a Greek who must have been responsible for shooting over four thousand elephant in his lifetime. He had a contract to produce three hundred and fifty elephants a year, as food for the mines in the Belgian Congo, for twelve years. My informant told me that he could remember the days when elephant used to pass the borders of the Belgian Congo, the Sudan, and Uganda, in herds of thousands; whereas the biggest herd I have passed over is the Bor herd of about five hundred. There is no doubt that the last thirty years have seen the elephant of Africa vastly reduced by the frantic hunt for food and ivory'.

Restriction to one elephant a year from any rifle in the Sudan later ensured that the herds were not decimated and that only the old bulls with the better ivory bore the brunt of the attack. Nevertheless, despite more stringent control measures throughout central eastern Africa, the fauna continued to dwindle.

Up until 30 or 40 years ago all the common species of antelope were distributed throughout the Zande country of the Sudan in the parts suitable to them—water-buck, Uganda kob, Jackson's harte-beest, dik-dik, duiker, oribi and so on. Wart-hog were common and the red bush pig a pest as were buffalo. Eland were said to be found in the Vagba forest along the south bank of the Sue. Rhinoceroses were not uncommon and there were a few herds of giraffe. As the local people considered that eating their meat caused leprosy they were not molested. Lion, too, were common as were leopards, hyaenas and wild dogs. The first were liked as providers of meat for the people and no cases of man-eaters were known. The only complaint was on one occasion when a lioness settled down near a path and threatened passers by. Soon afterwards, however, she moved off with a cub in her mouth, which explained her aggressive attitude.

Hippos abounded in the rivers but bongo, tiang and reed-buck were uncommon. Ivory declined in size and quantity after about 1910. Before this time the chiefs used to sell a lot of fine tusks that had been buried in past times to keep them safe from raiders, a custom no doubt dating from slaving days. In those days tusks weighing 80 lbs or 90 lbs were not rare and 50-60 lb tusks were common. It was soon learned that tusks under 15 lbs in weight or cow ivory were confiscated and such were sent clandestinely into the Congo or the traders in Wau who quickly made them into bracelets or smuggled them down to Omdurman.

During the rains, elephants would turn up in the most unlikely places: one was shot in a garden in Yambio and they used to visit the head of the Gomonaikpe, a mile or less from Tembura. South of the Sue there were large herds and for some years it was impossible to get a lone runner to go from Tembura to Yambio, on account of one which was always near the main road. These herds used to migrate northwards from the Congo border in the late rains and back again in the dry weather (p. 94).

In 1924, C. Christy wrote: 'The case of the White Rhinoceros seems a fairly hopeless one. . . . In the British Sudan comparatively few individuals now survive. . . . In the Meridi and Yambio districts in 1916 I came across them many times during my long roads in the bush. The fact that I saw two or three animals with horn of what seemed to me extraordinary length is perhaps evidence that there at least they are not molested. The forested and rocky islands up and down the Ituri river are favourite places for elephants. They are more or less safe retreats in which solitary old bulls and sometimes small herds hide in the daytime. During 1911, . . . an English elephant hunter, with a small canoe and two men, and almost no equipment, shot twenty-eight elephants'.

Ten years later, in 1934, about 250,000 head of lechwe were still living in the valley of the River Kafue in Zambia and another 150,000 round Lake Bangweolo. Today they have been reduced to a tenth of their former numbers.

In this chapter I have tried chiefly by means of quotations from the accounts of travellers and others, to indicate how game populations have declined in eastern Africa. This decline has been due partly to excess hunting with fire-arms, both by Europeans and Africans, and partly to the indirect effects of human settlement closing migration routes, altering the vegetation, introducing and disseminating disease and generally making life intolerable for game animals: these factors are discussed in the following chapter.

CHAPTER IV

FIRE-ARMS AND HUMAN SETTLEMENT

In Chapter II it was pointed out that native hunting methods are not sufficiently effective to endanger populations of game animals. In the last chapter I tried to indicate the extent to which the African fauna has declined since the advent of Europeans. Here I shall discuss the various factors that are jointly responsible for this decline. They include the effects of fire-arms, in the hands both of Europeans and Africans, poaching, human settlement in its various aspects, and the introduction of disease by imported domestic stock.

Big-Game hunting

It is impossible to distinguish between the effects on game populations of shooting and of human settlement, because the two are almost synonymous. Professional, or market hunting, will seldom exterminate a species, because it becomes uneconomic unless game is abundant. But the farmer or stockbreeder can always find time to kill the odd animal living on his land. Indeed, to be fair to the great hunters of the past, it should be emphasised that the majority of them not only possessed exceptional physique and courage but were unselfish, gentle and had a deep understanding of and sympathy for their quarry. Many of them were wonderful shots. Those reared on the Karoo, for example, made it a point of honour not to shoot the great bustard anywhere but through the neck—say at 100 yards, and many could do the same to an ostrich as it ran past.

Hunting yarns and adventures lie somewhat beyond the scope of this book and, in Chapter VI, I have quoted as far as possible examples which illustrate the character of the game rather than of its hunters. For accounts of some of the adventures of the latter, the reader is referred to an excellent book by D. D. Lyell (1924) as well as to the hunters' own reminiscences. As an example of one of these characters, it is, however, perhaps worth giving Sir Samuel Baker's opinion of W. Cotton Oswell who lived and hunted about 1850: 'Oswell was not merely a shooter, but he had been attracted towards Africa by his natural love of exploration, and the investigation of untrodden ground. He was absolutely the first white man who had appeared upon the scene in many portions of South Africa which are now well known. . . . He was a first-rate horseman, and all his shooting was from the saddle, or by dismounting for the shot after he had run his game to bay'.

Other great hunters included Baker himself, C. H. Stigand, F. C. Selous, A. H. Neumann, Cornwallis Harris, R. J. Cunningham, W. D. M. Bell and C. R. S. Pitman, to mention but a few. R. G. Gordon-Cumming was quite exceptional in being cruel and sadistic. Several times he fired as many as 35 rounds at an elephant before it died. Once he was shooting at one from 11.30 a.m. till sunset, and admitted firing 57 rounds before the animal expired. Unlike other hunters, he usually opened fire at 100 yards or more, which was probably why he did not kill cleanly, as he used only small charges of powder. Even so, the barrel of his favourite weapon once burst, which shows that he was not without some justification for this. The following is an extract from his book, *Five Years of a Hunter's Life in the far Interior of South Africa* (1850).

'I came in full view of the largest bull elephant I had ever seen. He stood broadside to me, at upward of one hundred yards, and his attention at the moment was occupied with the dogs, which, having winded him, were rushing past in search of his exact position, while the old fellow seemed to gaze at their unwonted appearance with surprise. Halting my horse, I fired at his shoulder, and secured him with a single shot. The ball caught him high upon the shoulder-blade, rendering him instantly dead lame; and before the echo of the bullet could reach my ear, I plainly saw that the elephant was mine. The dogs now came up and barked around him, but, finding himself incapacitated, the old fellow seemed determined to take it easy, and, limping slowly to a neighbouring tree, he remained stationary, eyeing his pursuers with a resigned and philosophic air.

'I resolved to devote a short time to the contemplation of this noble elephant before I should lay him low; accordingly, having off-saddled the horses beneath a shady tree which was to be my quarters for the night and ensuing day, I quickly kindled a fire and put on the kettle, and in a very few minutes my coffee was prepared. There I sat in my forest home, coolly sipping my coffee, with one of the finest elephants in Africa awaiting my pleasure beside a neighbouring tree. . . .

'Having admired the elephant for a considerable time, I resolved to make experiments for vulnerable points, and, approaching very near, I fired several bullets at different parts of his enormous skull. These did not seem to affect him in the slightest; he only acknowledged the shots by a "salaam-like" movement of his trunk, with the point of which he gently touched the wound with a striking and peculiar action. Surprised and shocked to find that I was only tormenting and prolonging the sufferings of the noble beast, which bore his trials with such dignified composure, I resolved to finish the proceeding with all possible dispatch: accordingly I opened fire upon him from the left side, aiming behind the shoulder; but even there it was long before my bullets seemed to take effect.

'I first fired six shots with the two-grooved, which must have eventually proved mortal, but, as yet, he evinced no visible distress; after which I fired three shots at the same part with the Dutch six-pounder. Large tears now trickled from his eyes, which he slowly shut and opened; his colossal frame quivered convulsively, and falling on his side, he expired. The tusks of this elephant were beautifully arched and were the heaviest I had yet met with, averaging 90 lb. weight apiece. In case any fair reader may misinterpret my motive for killing this elephant in the manner which I describe, I will remark that my object was *not* to uselessly torture the animal, but to put an end to its life and pain in the quickest manner possible. I had often lamented having to inflict so many wounds on the noble animals before they fell. To many sportsmen, or persons understanding such matters, this explanation is not required'.

Clearly, most people today are neither 'sportsmen' in this sense, nor would they accept such an explanation. Fortunately, this kind of behaviour is a thing of the past and, even then, it was exceptional.

The power of modern firearms is well illustrated by the following extract from the Annual Report of the Uganda Game & Fisheries Department for 1950: 'Two elephants were killed recently in Achole with one shot. The bullet passed through the brain of one and entered the neck of the second, killing both instantly. Such incidents are not uncommon with high-velocity rifles'. Conditions were very different in the old days when hunters used double 14 or 16-bore muzzle-loading shotguns with barrels cut down to a length of 24 ins. to make them handy in thick cover. The bullets were spherical and hardened for penetration.

W. C. Oswell, who went to South Africa in 1844 and has already been mentioned in this chapter, used a double 10-bore gun (which he afterwards lent to Baker for his expedition to the source of the Nile). Oswell had several narrow escapes, on one occasion from two white rhinos, one of which he shot. When he approached, the wounded animal drove its horn into the flank of his horse throwing it into the air with the force of the blow. Oswell's head was badly cut on the stirrup iron but, luckily, the rhino went off. Oswell followed it on another horse, killed it and returned to despatch his own injured horse. On another occasion he was gored in the thigh by a female rhinoceros. In 1848-9, in company with Dr. David Livingstone,

Oswell travelled through the Kalahari Desert and discovered Lake Ngami.[1]

Cornwallis Harris (1844) was even more of an explorer than a hunter but, like Henry Faulkner and W. C. Baldwin whose book, *African Hunting—from Natal to the Zambesi* (1863) first attracted F. C. Selous to Africa, he was also an excellent shot. William Finaughty killed 133 elephants on one trek, but the most he ever shot in one day was 10. A. H. Neumann, perhaps the greatest elephant hunter of all time, once killed 14 in one day and 11 in another. On one occasion his rifle misfired and he was badly hurt by an elephant which knelt on him and jabbed its tusk through his arm and between his ribs. Other great hunters of more recent times include R. J. Cunningham, Captain C. R. S. Pitman and Captain R. J. D. Salmon. The two latter, being game wardens, have carried out most of their hunting in the course of their duties in elephant control.

If shooting were confined to professional hunters, its effect on game populations would be comparatively slight, as I have said, but when all the local inhabitants, Europeans and African, join in, the situation becomes more serious. Shooting is then not a sport but a means of winning honour, food and wealth.

Thus, Captain M. S. Wellby (1901) complained that the Abyssinian method of hunting elephant was quite opposed to his own ideas of sport, 'for from a safe distance an entire party of fifty or a hundred strong pepper the victims with volleys, and sometimes meet with success. An Abyssinian who has killed an elephant is looked upon in the country as a man of some parts. Menelik himself on one occasion shot one, and there were rejoicings in consequence. I was told that he fired the first shot, and then three hundred men fired the second. . . .'.

Arnold Hodson, writing about 1929, said much the same. 'The Abyssinian's idea of sport is totally different from ours. To him an immature elephant with no tusks counts just the same as a hundred-pound tusker with us. A Dajazmatch who shall be nameless, amused me much at Maja by giving me an account of an unsuccessful elephant hunt he once made on the Orno River. He told me, "We found a big elephant there one day. I had two hundred men with me and we all opened fire on him, but he went on running and running. We followed after for several hours, but shot all our ammunition away. We saw lots of blood, but never got him. Are they not bad animals!".'

The Ethiopians were not the only people to use massed fire arms against big game. 'The people of the southern hills, bordering the Dar Homr, were at one time great elephant hunters. Their usual

[1] Lyell, 1924.

method was to encircle a herd and then concentrate the fire of their old Remington rifles on one or two of the nearest beasts. These elephant hunts generally ended in a sea of gore, but, during recent years, have become much less frequent owing to these mighty animals being very scarce all over Southern and Western Kordofan due to their wholesale slaughter by the Messeria tribe. A few Nuba in the extreme south-west have copied from the Arabs the method of riding down the giraffe on horseback and killing it with spears as it runs, but in the majority of cases this animal is hunted and despatched by arranging a trap which cuts the hamstrings'.[2]

Nor were Europeans innocent of similar behaviour. In 1924, D. D. Lyell wrote: 'When I went from Nyasaland to British East Africa in 1911 for a short trip, I saw the veld between Kyabe and Deepdale Drift full of fired cartridge cases, showing that a great number of parties had been blazing ammunition at game'. With considerable acumen, he added: 'Vast changes have taken place in Africa during the last 100 years. Improvement in firearms may not have had such an effect on the reduction of animals as the constant noise and disturbance in their haunts'.

Sir Alfred Pease (1913) recorded a hunter who killed in one place some 94 Soemmerring gazelle and left a plain covered with rotting carcasses, not to mention cripples, without getting a record head. He added: 'Some hideous work has been done in the name of sport'.

Of a place near Chiramo, Edouard Foá (1894) wrote as follows: 'Opposite, on the left bank of the river, there was indeed a plain where unfortunate buffaloes, persisting in stopping there, were slaughtered, sportsmen of the locality firing upon them while smoking pipes in hammocks carried by shrieking men in white shirts and red caps. The local administration ended by forbidding this butchery; but there were still pseudo-sportsmen who killed in a morning seven or eight buffaloes without troubling themselves even to take away the bodies which they left to the vultures'. Near Mossamudes, Angola, in 1879, van Zyls stampeded 104 elephants into a marsh and killed them all whilst they were bogged.

Many of the old hunters gave up following elephants when they began to inhabit more densely wooded country where tsetse flies abounded, because it was impossible to take horses there and it is not only infinitely harder work following elephants on foot, but much more dangerous.[3] Considerations such as these, however, did not deter the African who was just as short-sighted as the European about game conservation and often even more courageous, as we have

[2]Fife, 1927.

[3]Livingstone was told that a European who hunted elephant on foot would die soon—guns were unreliable in those days!

already seen. For example, in some districts the natives killed elephants in enormous numbers and without discrimination, not for the tusks merely, but for the meat and hides. In 1895 the Homr and Rizighat Arabs killed about 800 elephants. The Homr killed 87 in one day (Soudan Reports for 1895, p. 129).

A century ago, the Boers set trap guns to destroy night-prowling 'vermin', such as 'hyaenas that were too persistent in their attempts on the meat supply or on leather gear, lions that defied killing in day time and the wary leopard. Any old musket that would stand a heavy charge was lashed firmly to two poles or a tree stump at a distance from the ground that was adjusted to the height of the intended victim'. It was convenient to attach the bait, a big piece of meat, to the muzzle or it was staked lightly to the ground a little way in front of the gun and high enough to prevent jackals and other small carnivores from taking it. Bait and trigger were connected by a cord which ran through ramrod loops and so arranged that a tug on the bait discharged the gun.[4]

The primary objects of the chase in those days were ivory, ostrich feathers, rhinoceros horns, hippo teeth, hides and meat—mostly the Boers shot for hides and wasted the meat, however. Elephants were hunted on horse back and from pits dug in the ground near water-holes. These were 10 ft. long, 3 ft. deep and 30 ins. wide. Heavy logs, strong enough to support an elephant, crossed the central part and there were seats at the ends so that a man could sit in each with his head above ground. Before long, however, elephants learned to reconnoitre their water-holes before coming to drink!

Until recently, gun traps were used in the Sudan and even more extensively in Ethiopia. The bait was a sheep's or goat's head and a rifle, resting on a forked stick, was pushed through this from the rear.[5] The African has not been slow in learning European methods of destruction.

For better or worse, Africans and Europeans are now bound together by remorse for the past and hope for the future. Wherever Europeans appeared, they uprooted or enslaved the natives, claimed the best land for themselves and drove out the wild animals. In fact, they behaved much in the same way as did warlike tribes such as the Zulus to their weaker neighbours. I do not intend to pass judgement or apportion blame to either, as I consider both have behaved equally stupidly. Nor, however, do I not think that there is any reason to suppose that the Governments of newly independent African states will do any worse than did their predecessors. They may quite possibly do better for, traditionally, the African recognises

[4]Tabler, 1955.
[5]Brocklehurst, 1931.

that the fauna is as much a part of a country's wealth as the fertility of the soil, whereas the European goes from one extreme to the other. First he treats wild animals as a menace to be exterminated and then gives them absolute protection so that their numbers reach pest proportions and control measures become necessary.

Elephant control

At the present time, the elephant is in no danger of extermination in eastern Africa. Indeed, in certain areas, the problem is not to prevent its disappearance, but to keep the number of elephants within reasonable limits. Conservation abounds in paradoxes and, although the range of the African elephant has been very greatly reduced during the last 50 years, and there are fears that the animal may become extinct outside game parks, there are some places where there are too many elephants.

These include Bunyore in north-west Uganda where herds of up to 1,000 have frequently been seen from the air and the total elephant population is probably about 12,000 in an area of some 3,000 square miles. In the Budongo forest considerable damage is done to crops and timber. Although elephants use their tusks with remarkable dexterity to rend the bark from trees, the actual harm done to woodlands is for the most part indirect. Trees 'barked' by elephants are more vulnerable to grassland fires than undamaged specimens and their death allows more light to penetrate into the forest edge. The result of this is that grass tends to grow which, in turn, encourages more fires: consequently there is a tendency for the woodland to degenerate into savannah.[6]

As long ago as 1927, Captain C. S. R. Pitman wrote in the Report of the Uganda Game Department that 'the annual toll taken by Government action, licence-holders and others is easily covered by the normal, annual increase'. An important factor too, had been the presence of sleeping sickness, as a result of which the area under consideration was closed to settlement in 1912, and the subsequent establishment of game reserves and the Murchison Falls National Park. A somewhat similar situation occurs at Tsavo in Kenya where overgrazing and soil erosion are directly due to over-abundance of elephants in a limited area.

In 1912, rifles were issued to natives in Uganda for elephant control purposes and, although the practice was discontinued in 1917, still some 20,328 rounds of ammunition were distributed. In the Report of the Uganda Game Department for 1923 it was estimated that the country held 30,000 elephants and that, allowing for 1,000 killed by man each year and a smaller death rate from natural causes,

[6]Hillaby, J. (1961) New Scientist, 12, 736-8.

these numbers would be doubled in 30 years. In fact, by 1936 the annual death rate from all causes had reached 2,300 and the population was still increasing.[7] It is not sufficient for sportsmen merely to kill the big tuskers. Elephants with small tusks often do great damage and are usually more fertile.

Where it is protected, the hippopotamus, like the elephant, may increase so rapidly in numbers that it causes overgrazing and becomes a pest. The obvious solution to problems such as these is to crop surplus animals and thus provide a welcome source of meat for local populations whose normal diet is otherwise deficient in protein. Indeed, game ranching becomes inseparable from game conservation and is discussed in Chapter X.

Tsetse control

The nineteen twenties and thirties were among the worst decades for the plains game of central eastern Africa for, during this period hunters in cars, armed with modern rifles, killed off in a few hours more creatures than they could have stalked in a month. In addition, many animals were slaughtered in the interests of tsetse control.

Between 1932-59, no less than 550,594 game were shot in Rhodesia alone, excluding the many beasts wounded, but not killed outright by inexperienced marksmen anxious to claim their bounty. In one year 3,219 baboons, 61 wild dogs, 35 hyaenas, 19 leopards, 4 lions, 55 elephants, 8 rhinos, 312 zebras, 950 bush pigs, 4,503 wart-hogs, 377 buffaloes, 50 wildebeest, 301 water-buck, 777 reedbuck, 1,357 sable and 306 roan antelopes, 291 elands, 4,937 kudus, 5 of the rare nyalas, 1,788 bushbuck, 2,219 impalas, 12,566 duikers, 1,037 klipspringers, 134 oribi and 1,206 oryx—a total of 36,552 animals—were butchered.[8] Certainly the slaughter of game shows some tangible results and is simple and cheap, but the long term efficacy of this method of tsetse eradication is questionable.

South Africa, Tanganyika and Uganda have also from time to time suffered from tsetse control schemes, during which hundreds of thousands of wretched ungulates have been butchered. In Natal alone, half a million animals were slaughtered during the twenties. In Uganda, several pockets of carefully preserved black rhinoceros have been sacrificed, along with some of the few surviving herds of eland, roan antelope and kob. In all, some 60,000 antelopes were destroyed there during the years 1952-62 without any economic use being made of the meat and hides.

I do not propose to write at length about the problems of tsetse control, but the method of mass butchery can only be regarded with

[7]Melland, 1938.
[8]Grzimek, 1960.

horror and revulsion, especially as it has little scientific justification.[9] It has been shown that wart-hogs and bush pigs may supply up to 88 per cent of the blood sucked by tsetse flies in East Africa. Buffaloes account for a further 5 per cent. Roan antelopes, kudus and bushbuck between them can yield another 15 per cent while domestic cattle, sheep and goats are also regularly bitten. The most common grazing animals, such as hartebeests, topi antelopes, zebras and wildebeest are not bitten at all, while tsetse flies rarely attack eland, duikers, water-buck, impalas, baboons, monkeys, dogs, cats, hyaenas and birds.[10]

Poaching

With the establishment of game reserves and the ban on hunting except under licence, a new crime—poaching—was created. Two of the more serious factors that threaten the extermination of African game are the use of motor-cars for hunting and the immense number of muzzle-loading guns[11] in the possession of African natives. Poachers also use traps of various kinds, poisoned arrows and so on.

A recent development used by poachers in the arid area behind the East African coastline consists of a bow with a poisoned arrow which is discharged when a string is touched. This device almost exterminated the game between Malindi and the Tsavo River. Also in recent years, blocks of wood studded with poisoned darts have been buried in the tracks used by elephants and rhinoceroses. They are effective only against animals with large, soft feet but, if any such should tread on them, they are doomed.

Poachers use the traditional hunting methods described in Chapter II which are both wasteful and extremely cruel. In addition, intro-duction of steel wire, has given them a new and very effective weapon. Wire is cheap and can be strong enough to hold an elephant: two pieces of $\frac{1}{16}$in stranded steel wire can hold a full-grown buffalo. Long lines of wire nooses are laid out and zebra, wildebeest, antelope, elephant and rhinos get trapped by the leg or neck. The noose is attached to a tree stump or to a heavy log which the wretched animal can barely move. Its struggles tighten the wire which bites into the flesh, causing a festering wound so that the unfortunate beast dies a lingering, agonizing death. Wire does not distinguish between males, females and young, but it is silent and, when used in reserves, does not advertise the poacher like firearms do.

One can scarcely blame the protein-hungry native who kills for food. This is a minor menace, however. Most poaching on a big scale

[9]Glover, P. E. (1965) I.U.C.N. Publ. (N.S.) No. 6, 84 pp.
[10]Weitz, B. & Glasgow, J. P. (1956) Trans. R. Soc. Trop. Med. Hyg. 50, 593-612.
[11]Ten years ago, over 30,000 muzzle-loaders were registered in Tanganyika and this number must have been far exceeded by that of illegally owned guns.

is directed towards the production of commercially valuable products such as ivory, leopard skins, rhino horns, and zebra tails for fly-whisks. From most of the tens of thousands of animals killed annually by poachers in eastern Africa today, the trophies are cut out and the meat simply left to rot.

Then there are the commercial venison hunters who shoot at night the animals dazzled by the headlights of their cars. And the soldiers who turn machine-guns on elephants, zebras and gazelles. Africa is a large continent, while greed and stupidity are hard to control in any country.

Disease

About 1880, the cattle disease rinderpest was accidentally brought across the Red Sea and introduced into eastern Africa. From cattle it infected the wild game which, in turn, re-introduced it to cattle. So serious was this that many pastoralists turned to agriculture, thereby increasing the population pressure in forested areas such as Kilimanjaro and Meru.

The first great rinderpest epidemic began in 1891. Buffalo died in thousands and occasionally dead giraffe, water-buck and bush-buck were seen. Eland, kudu and roan antelope also suffered. At Ngomini in N.E. Kitui which was a great cattle centre before the epidemic, only a few score beasts survived and the desiccated corpses of many thousands of victims were piled up like walls outside the villages.

This outbreak was the worst epidemic known in the recent history of Africa; it spread rapidly south through what was then German East Africa, crossed the Zambesi, reached Bulawayo about 1895 and by the end of 1896 it had reached the Cape. During the last year of the visitation its progress was remarkably rapid, viz., about 1,000 miles; it was probably spread to a great extent by the transport riders. Since that devastating attack there have been minor epidemics of the disease. In 1904, eland were dying of it near Naivasha, and the Masai then lost over 600 head of stock. Although sporadic outbreaks still occur, the disease is now well in hand.[12]

When F. J. Jackson (1894) returned from Uganda in July 1890, he saw, between Baringo and Naivasha, herds varying in size from 100 to 600 buffalo six times in a single day. Count Teleki, while at Njemps in January 1888, shot no less than 53 buffalo in a month according to Höhnel (1894). In the same district, in 1893, J. W. Gregory (1896) did not see a single individual. Five years before, the buffalo had been almost the commonest of the big game of East Africa. 'The explanation has been supplied by Gedge, who followed Jackson a few months later. Several times a day his caravan had to diverge from its path, to

[12]Hobley, C. W. (1922). *Proc. Zool. Soc. Lond.* **1922**, 1-15.

avoid the stench from a rotting carcase—in fact he saw fifteen in one day; but he did not see a single living buffalo. Cattle disease had swept through the country, and destroyed them all'.

Sir Gerald Portal (1894) described the effect of rinderpest in Kenya as follows: 'The absence of game, the paucity of birds, and the eternal wild sighing of the giant juniper trees all had a somewhat eerie and depressing influence, deepened by the sight of hundreds and hundreds of skulls, skeletons, and scattered bones of the unfortunate buffaloes, which only two or three years ago used to range in vast herds over these mountains. A dreadful plague which, spreading southwards from Somaliland, overran, two years ago, the whole of East Africa, furnishes one of the most melancholy instances in the annals of natural history, of the sudden and almost complete extermination of a whole race of noble animals. Three years ago the magnificent African buffalo roamed in tens, and even hundreds of thousands over the Masai plains, over the Mau Mountains, over, in fact, the whole of what is called British and German East Africa; but now a traveller may wander for months in all the most likely or most inaccessible places, and see nothing of the buffalo except his horns and whitened bones scattered over the plain, or lying literally in heaps near tempting springs and cool watering places, to which the poor brutes had flocked to quench their consuming thirst, and to die. In South Africa, the buffalo is still to be found, I believe, in some numbers, but there he is rapidly being exterminated from the south by the advancing rifles of civilisation, while on the other side there is reason to fear that this same dread plague, having done its fatal work in the east, is steadily and relentlessly pursuing its course southwards, so that unless in the meantime the virulence of the epidemic mercifully dies out, the South African buffalo will inevitably share the fate of his northern cousin. The stately eland, which was never so numerous as the buffalo, appears to have succumbed to the same plague, and the natives assert, though with what truth I know not, that there is not one left in East Africa. . . .'.

A few years later, Major A. St H. Gibbons (1904), writing of his 1898-1900 expedition, said that, after proceeding through the Kariba gorge, 'the numerous buffalo skulls encountered on the veldt showed that the district had been ravaged by the rinderpest epidemic of two years previously. Prior to that cruel visitation this must have been a favourite resort of game, for everything was in favour of its having been so—the country, the sparseness of population, and the comparative abundance of game still surviving that most destructive of all scourges'.

It is fortunate that game populations have proved to be more resilient to disease than was at first realised. Nevertheless, by the introduction of epidemic diseases, civilisation for a time struck one of its harder blows against the wild game of eastern Africa.

After the havoc created by the rinderpest epidemic which reached South Africa in 1897-98, there were probably not more than about a dozen buffalo left in the old South African Sabi Reserve. Although the buffalo population north of the Olifants River and also that of the central district was largely built up by immigrants from Portuguese East Africa, the great herds that at present roam through most of the Kruger National Park illustrate clearly the inherent recuperative powers of this species after a natural catastrophe. The largest single herd now numbers over 1,500 individuals and there are several others of up to 800 animals. In contrast, eland, whose numbers had already been greatly reduced by African and European hunters were exterminated in the lowvelt. Fortunately, a few escaped in Portuguese East Africa whence they repopulated the Park and now number about 450.[13]

In addition to rinderpest, which is caused by a virus, other epidemic diseases that sometimes ravage the game and domestic animals of Africa include foot and mouth, anthrax and nagana. The first of these is caused by rikettsias, the second by bacteria and the last by protozoan trypanosomes. Mention should also be made of helminth parasites, which become more serious when there is overgrazing, and toxicosis resulting from tick infestation.

Especially in very dry years, when grazing is scarce and the plains are dusty, outbreaks of anthrax occur among the game, the principal species to suffer being Coke's hartebeest. The last serious outbreak to be identified was in 1905, when several thousand head of game died on the Athai plains of Kenya.

Anthrax is frequently disseminated by vultures that feed on dead animals and then contaminate with the deadly bacteria or their spores the watering places that they visit to drink. The excreta of vultures and other carrion eaters that have fed on anthrax carcasses are another important means of contamination of water and grazing with anthrax spores. Even the dung of non-susceptible animals which have fed on infected grazing or heavily infected pools may cause the pollution of uninfected grazing or water. Possibly herd animals like buffalo, elephant, and wart-hog that are fond of wallowing in mud can also carry infected mud from one waterhole to another. The carcasses of animals that die near waterholes may be opened by crocodiles and terrapins, thus infecting the water.

Control methods include burning of the vegetation, incinerating or burying carcasses and fencing off infected waterholes. Water can sometimes be disinfected, but it is not known if this may adversely

[13]Pienaar, U. de V. (1963) *Koedoe* No. 6, 1-37.

affect the internal flora of ruminants and cause metabolic disturbance. It is impractical to inject game animals with anthrax vaccine, but the administration of an oral vaccine through the drinking water is a distant possibility. The only effective and safe prophylactic measure is the building up of an immense stock of game.[14]

Pleuro-pneumonia is rarely absent from the herds of Masai cattle that graze in the plains of Kenya but, curiously enough, there is no record of the disease attacking game. Cases are known in which eland and buffalo graze over the same land as cattle infected with this disease and are apparently unaffected.

About 1906, an epidemic of what is believed to have been distemper broke out among the jackals of the Athai plains, and large numbers died. A year or two later, the same disease was recorded from the Rift Valley and then from Laikipia. It is not known, however, whether the disease is endemic or has been introduced by civilization.[15]

In addition to diseases and pests attributable to or disseminated by human activities, wild animals are affected by many natural plagues. For example, in 1961 there was a devastating drought in the Ngorongoro crater which was followed by unusually heavy and prolonged rain. At the swampy margins of the lake, nine consecutive generations of stable flies, *Stomoxys* spp. bred, and the population built up to fantastic numbers. *Stomoxys* is not normally particularly harmful, but there were so many that they killed many antelope and even lions. One of these was seen with its side half scratched away and caked with blood. Before the plague, roughly sixty lions inhabited the crater but afterwards there were only fifteen.[16]

Taking everything into consideration, however, disease is rare amongst game and serious epidemics uncommon. Directly an animal becomes sick, it either leaves the herd or is driven out. Being alone and dull with sickness it readily falls a prey to predators and scavengers and little is left as a source of infection to others of its own species.

Agriculture, ranching and industry

A hundred years ago, perhaps three million elephants lived in Africa and there was ample food and space for them all. But, when the virgin land began to be cultivated, not only was less natural food available for the great pachyderms, but they were tempted by the tasty plantations of the farmers who naturally took defensive measures. Between 1880 and 1910, over 2 million elephants were shot and, today, there is food and space left for only some 300,000.

[14]Pienaar, U. de V. (1961) *Koedoe* No. 4, 4-16.
[15]Hobley, C. W. (1922). *Proc. Zool. Soc. Lond.* **1922**, 1-15.
[16]Huxley, 1964.

When the space available to game is much reduced, a danger arises from the fact that local drought, or some other disaster is always liable to destroy the wild life of a particular region. In the past, repopulation could always take place from the surrounding country-side but, when this reserve has been eliminated, droughts and so on become potentially much more dangerous.

It is easy to pass judgement in matters over which one is not directly concerned. Naturally, as a zoologist, I am biased in favour of the game. No doubt if I were a farmer I should feel very differently. As P. Ness wrote in 1929: 'But then [1906], as now, the settlers in Kenya had as their chief interest farming in all its branches, which in the outlying parts had its drawbacks and its hardships. . . . I realised what it meant to plough up virgin soil when on our coffee farm I saw our thirty-two oxen slaving to plough not only unturned land but high grass and bushes as they came in the way, brought up short now and then by a deeply concealed tree-stump overlooked in the stumping'.

Who, after years of gruelling work in a harsh climate could stand by impassionately while the fruits of his labours were devastated by elephants or other game? Again, much has been written of the evils of grass burning. But the other side of the picture is given by Sir Samuel Baker (1890).

'The distressing months, when a continuance of rain has en-couraged a giant growth of herbage, cannot be appreciated by those who have not experienced the block of vegetation. The entire country becomes impassable, being clothed in a dense mass of coarse grass from 8 to 10 feet high. By degrees this ripens, and when the dry weather has continued for two or three months, it becomes highly inflammable, and is fired in all directions by the inhabitants. When a strong north wind is blowing, the sight is most impressive, as nothing appears to check the flames. The fire rushes onward with wild delight, crackling the hollow cones, licking the dried leaves off lofty branches, and roaring like a heavy gale as it drives forward in its destructive course, leaving the blackened ground behind as clean as a velvet path. An immense extent of country may be cleared within a few days, if the grass is carefully ignited to windward, and it is a mystery how the wild animals arrange their retreat before the annual conflagration. I imagine that they are well aware of certain places of refuge in the dry beds of rivers, where the experience of the past has assured them of security. At any rate, they save themselves, and reappear upon the scene within a very few days after the fire has destroyed all the pasturage'.

The real threat to wildlife in Africa is caused by the recent enormous increase in human population resulting from the introduction of modern sanitation and medicine and the abolition of slave-trading and inter-tribal warfare. In 1890, there were around 500,000 people living in Southern Rhodesia. Today the population there is nearer three million, and other countries have shown similar gains. This has meant that farming has had to expand and game animals have therefore been eliminated. Dangerous animals have been shot: in one part of Kenya, 1,000 rhinoceroses were killed to open up a new area to farming. Today, only 11,000-13,500 black and 2,500-3,000 white rhinos are left alive.

Increased population leads to industrialization which, again, is incompatible with big game. When the Kariba dam was built 51,000 people were evacuated from the area doomed to be flooded, but hundreds of thousands of wild animals were drowned in an area over 2,000 sq. miles—only a mere 6,000 were carried to safety despite the brave efforts of those who engaged in 'Operation Noah's Ark'. And we do not know how many of these could have survived the disruption of their lives, the involuntary eviction from their homes and, most harmful of all, the separation from their social groups and the upset of their natural behavioural hierarchies.

Much of Africa consists of rough, dry country that is quite unsuitable for farming. But here the land is utilised by vast numbers of domestic cattle which cause over-grazing and ultimately soil erosion. In Rhodesia, the number of African-owned cattle has increased forty-fold during the same period in which the human population has increased six fold. Most of these cattle are economically worthless, but are kept for their prestige value, to serve as marriage dowries and as sacrifies to the ancestral spirits.

The same is true of other parts of the continent and cattle owners will defend their stock against predators with great bravery. Major Henry Darley, self-styled 'Explorer, Ivory Hunter and formerly British Frontier Agent at Maji in Abyssinia' gives the following account (1926) of how a little boy, herding sheep in Northern Uganda, fought a lioness, single handed, after it had killed some of his flock. He was 'armed with a small spear, and a shield made of wicker-work, about eighteen inches long by nine inches wide—a sort of toy shield. He ran straight up to the lioness, and holding his shield in front of him, speared her in the neck, just as she rose on her hind legs to claw his left arm with both forepaws almost from shoulder to waist. Undeterred, the boy speared her again. The lioness turned round, went a few paces, then curled up and died. The boy went over to the lioness, satisfied himself that she was dead, and then, walking straight up to me, and holding out his arm, streaming with blood, without change of countenance, said: "Give me some 'dawa' (medicine) for these scratches". I was amazed at his fortitude, but curtly replied: "Go up to the camp, there is plenty there".'

In general, pastoralists are not hunters except for prestige purposes. For example, the Tatoga will exhibit trophies such as an elephant or buffalo tail, or a lion's mane. Indeed, game reserves today are largely situated in areas that have been preserved from agriculture by pastoralism or tsetse.

Wild game do, however, conflict with cattle directly by competing with them for food and indirectly by infecting them with disease. Moreover, cattle ranching requires the construction of fences, corrals and pens. These may result in cutting off game animals such as buffalo and wildebeest from their sources of water so that they perish. On the other hand elephant, zebra and giraffe often break down fences, causing costly damage, whilst eland, impala and other antelope, which can leap over fences, are not involved either way.

Apart from trypanosomiasis or nagana, many other diseases can spread from game to cattle and vice versa. The wildebeest carries a disease called malignant catarrh, or *snotsiekte*, the buffalo harbours tick fever and many game animals are infected with foot-and-mouth disease. Conversely, the cattle plague rinderpest was introduced into eastern Africa by cattle as we have seen.

Livestock owners naturally tend to exaggerate the risk of disease to their animals but, with proper care of the cattle herds, this danger can be reduced to a tolerable level. Competition for food as often as not does not take place because many game animals have food preferences widely different from those of cattle. Indeed, their presence in an area can actually improve the food for cattle by keeping down the encroachment of shrubs and weeds.

As a result of the 'Ground-nuts Scheme', in 1948, thick deciduous bush was cleared at Kongwa, Tanganyika. This revealed artificial rainponds as occur in southern Masailand, indicating that the area had once been open to pastoralism. Possibly overgrazing resulted in the formation of bush penetrable only by rhinos and elephants. Clearing of the bush for agricultural purposes may result in the formation of glades which attract elephant and buffaloes which, in turn, push the bush back still further.

Finally, as Prof. Raymond F. Dasmann (1964) has so ably demonstrated in his magnificent little book, *African Game Ranching*, wild animals are potentially far more productive than exotic cattle. It seems obvious that with proper understanding, there should always be room in Africa for agriculture, farming and for wild game.

Hippopotamus traps. From David and Charles Livingstone (1865).

CHAPTER V

BEHAVIOUR AND MIGRATION

JUST over 300 miles south-east of Khartoum lies the beautiful, but little-known Dinder National Park in the Fung District of Blue Nile Province. To get there, you drive to Wad Medani, past the blue irrigation canals of the Gezira along endless corrugated desert tracks, and then cross the Blue Nile over the Sennar Dam. South of Abu Hashim, on the 13th parallel N., the desert acacias give place abruptly to 'talih' (A. *fistula*) with vultures, bee-eaters, red-hussar and grivet monkeys in their branches and graceful gazelle crossing the track beneath. All around, guinea fowl can be heard calling among the trees. In the 'Beit el-Wahash' (home of beasts) there are vast herds of delicate reed-buck, bush-buck, sombre, stocky water-buck with massive horns, roan antelope, wart-hogs and ostrich that stretch like Panzer divisions to the hazy horizon.

Such mixing of quite unrelated species comes at first somewhat as a surprise to the ecologist who is accustomed to the idea that each species should occupy its own particular habitat to which it is specialised. No doubt the explanation is that throughout much of their lives the different species are indeed separate, but that they come together at certain times at places, such as water-holes, salt-licks and the like. Those that migrate to the Dinder river during the dry season each year move back across the border into Ethiopia during the rains.

Before human settlement blocked their progress, restricting them to game reserves and unpopulated regions, the game animals of eastern Africa moved with the seasons, crossing mountain ranges, wading through swamps and swimming rivers to reach the green savannah during the rainy season or to return to the forests with the onset of drought. As suggested in the previous chapter, human settlement and agriculture has adversely affected the game by blocking migration routes and restricting the wanderings of animals to limited areas in which overgrazing and soil erosion frequently occur.

Dr. J. W. Gregory (1896) commenting on the migrations and wanderings of big game gave an interesting picture of the speed and distances travelled. On one occasion he kept on the track of a herd of elephant on the Tana, and followed it all the way from Merifano till close to the coast. 'Several times we found tracks that could not have been made more than an hour previously, and once we heard them trumpeting and playing in a swamp beside our camp. But we never caught sight of them. The distance we followed them, however —only thirty miles—is little compared with that which hunters sometimes have to chase a herd. M. Foá, for example, in his recent book,[1] tells us how he tracked a herd of elephant for seventeen days, going as quickly as he could, before he finally came up with it. Other animals, such as the buffalo, travel in the same way. They walk slowly, feeding as they go, but often journeying twenty or thirty miles as the crow flies (or is supposed to fly), from one night's resting-place to the next. Only animals of considerable size can travel such distances, and since these journeys are necessary in Africa, the continent has gained the name of "the home of large mammals".'

Even today an immense, but little-known, game migration takes place each year between Kenya, south-west Ethiopia and the Sudan. The migration begins during the month of May when the swamps of the Upper Nile rise, and there is a general movement of animals south-east towards the arid Kenya border. The predominant species are white-eared kob, tiang and Mongalla gazelle. Zebra, Grant's gazelle, lesser eland and buffalo also move in considerable numbers. Some oryx and smaller numbers of giraffe, water-buck and roan antelope go along with the main body which is flanked by lion and the smaller predators.[2] In 1841, Ferdinand Werne reported in the same area herds of antelopes thousands strong, and said that they sounded like massed cavalry as they approached over the bare horizon.

Major Henry Darley (1926) described the same migration as follows: 'Continuing our journey westwards from Kisyangor, we found the whole country practically under water, and the game, which at that time of the year is driven to the higher ground from about the lower country, lying between the Sobat river and the White Nile, was the most wonderful sight I have ever seen. They came along in vast herds; thousands of them. They consisted mostly of hartebeest, white-eared kob, and little buck. They all seemed galloping in one direction, that is for the high land out of the mud. The natives had an exciting time running them down in the mud, and spearing all they wanted. They told me that the same herds return yearly to the same spot of high land, for it is here they are born. The lions were very numerous and went about openly in broad daylight. . . .

[1]Edouard Foá (1894) *Mes grandes Chasses dans l'Afrique centrale.* p. 285.
[2]Woodman, H. M. (1965) *Oryx* 8, 113-4.

Elephants too, were very numerous. They were, like the rest of the game, all bent on getting out of the mud'.

D. Zaphiro, a few years ago, described the migration from Ethiopia into northern Kenya in the following words: 'By the end of June, the plains are thickly populated not by hundreds but by thousands of the few species of game that customarily undertake the hazardous trek south. . . . It is here, checked from any further movement south by the exiguous tufts of the Turkana desert plains, that the game remains contentedly for three or four months until the desperate need of fresh grazing drives it north again in the fertile tracks of the retiring rains. . . . By September the area begins to clear again. In massed columns many miles long the game moves slowly and benignly north-wards, shielding its young from the voracious predators. The plains are given back to the burning heat. Herds of oryx beisa and Grant's gazelle, scattered into the outlying stretches by the migration, return now to the forsaken landscape. One can stroll through country whose every acre holds its complement of several hundred kob, and then abruptly, for no apparent reason, an invisible boundary is crossed and one sees nothing. One such boundary lies east of the Loelli landing strip. At the height of the migration this strip holds as many as three thousand kob: and yet only five hundred yards east one may search for days and not come across a single animal'.

The elephant sometimes endangers itself by its regular migratory habits. In different seasons it invariably seeks certain localities—open country during the rains, and forest during the dry season. Thus on Kilimanjaro, for instance, elephants move down the northern slopes of the Usambara range about April, and spread out through the Nyika plains almost to the coast. The wanderings of elephants throughout other parts of East Africa are likewise governed by food supply. Breeding herds, composed of animals from other herds, are said to travel from South Laikipia to the Aberdare mountains, then north-east to the Lorian swamps, north-west to Marsabit and then south again to the Aberdares. The round trip of some 400 miles takes three years: the young are born in Marsabit forest and the animals return with one-year old calves.

Hippos tend to migrate up river when the higher reaches are full and return to the mouth in the dry season. Rhinos, on the other hand, usually do not migrate. Nor do lions and other predators, except in pursuit of their prey; they change their hunting grounds according to the supply of game. Kudu and other antelope regularly migrate to summer feeding grounds, where they calve, returning to more favourable quarters for the winter. The quaggas of South Africa were alleged to migrate regularly in bands of two or three hundred.

Such movements are naturally inhibited or prevented by farming and other forms of land use; the small pockets in which many species of African big game now survive, may be relics lying on past migration routes.

Serengeti

In the Serengeti one may still see some of the remaining great herds of African plains game animals and their attendant predators. On the one hand the wildebeest, zebras, buffalo and numerous species of antelope; on the other lions, leopards, cheetahs, hyaenas, hunting dogs and jackals. Most of these plains game are migratory animals and are confined to arid regions with seasonal and uncertain rainfall. In order to survive, they have to migrate between their areas of wet-season and dry-season grazing. The former lie on the Serengeti plains in the lee of the Crater Highlands, the latter could be in the Highlands themselves, only about 15-25 km. away.

Unfortunately the animals follow a very much longer migration cycle which takes them outside the borders of the Serengeti National Park for a large part of every year. They follow the river valleys running from the plateau on which the plains lie down to Lake Victoria where there are alluvial pastures called 'dambos' or 'mbugas'. These are waterlogged during the rains so that there is little tree growth, but they provide good pasture during the dry season. The intervening migration routes are mostly through 'bush' country of various types, often heavily infested by tsetse.[3]

On the Serengeti plains, the game compete for pasture and water with the herds of the Masai, a pastoral tribe that lives on blood and milk from their cattle. The Masai have similar migratory habits as the game and, moreover, are steadily destroying the forests of the highlands, which almost certainly has an adverse effect on the water regime. Survival of the plains game therefore depends on sacrificing to them a share of both wet- and of dry-season grazing and probably also on maintaining the fertility of the intervening bush. Proposals to preserve their migration cycle involve an area of about 2,000 sq. miles but, if a new reserve could be established and fenced in, it might be possible to confine them to the plains and highlands with a short migration route between. They would then be protected from poaching and prevented from dying of hunger and thirst when all the timber around their water holes has been felled and their pastures overgrazed by Masai cattle.

The attention of the world has, however, recently been directed to the problem of Serengeti by the work of Professor Bernhard Grzimek (1960) and the tragic death of his son, Michael, who was

[3]Pearsall, W. H. (1962) in Le Gren, E. O. & Hodgate, M. W. (Eds.) The Exploitation of Natural Animal Populations. Oxford: Blackwell, pp. 343-57.

killed in 1959 when his aeroplane collided with a griffon vulture.[4]
I will therefore not discuss it further here, except to emphasise that
the nutritional requirements and preferences of the game must also
be catered for. Not all grassy plains are of equal value and the
nutritious plants only grow in special localities.

The migratory springbucks of south-east Africa

The most dramatic example of migration among African game is
afforded by the springbucks of south-east Africa which, at one time,
used on occasion to migrate in unbelievably vast numbers. This has
been the subject of a number of articles and books, in particular those
by W. C. Scully (1848), J. G. Millais (1899), Sir John Frazer (1922)
and T. C. Cronwright-Schreiner (1925), from which the following
information has been taken.

On the larger migrations, troops of 10,000-20,000 gathered together
into columns numbering hundreds of millions. Frazer recounts how
the town of Beaufort West was invaded about 1849 by a vast number
of springbuck, accompanied by blesbok, quaggas, wildebeest, eland
and 'antelopes of all sorts and kinds', which filled the streets and
gardens as far as could be seen. After three days the horde disappeared,
leaving the country 'looking as if a fire had passed over it'.

W. C. Scully described a vast emigration in which a wide column
took several days to pass the same spot, though it was not always of
the same density. Many died, especially old animals and kids, but
the survivors headed onwards until they reached the sea where they
were drowned in such numbers that the beach, for thirty miles, was
piled high with corpses. Scully thought that the migration was
prompted by thirst, but Heape (1931) suggested that it was more
probably due to food shortage after a population build up.

Other big treks of springbucks have been recorded by Millais and
Selous. Gordon-Cumming (1850) witnessed one between Cradock
and Colesberg. The animals streamed past his wagon 'like the flood
of some great river' and went 'through the neck in the hills in one
unbroken compact phalanx'. Subsequently he saw them covering
the plain and hillsides in a vast mass as far as he could see. He said
that, nevertheless, this was a small affair compared with what had
been seen by the Boers in earlier times.

In the words of Cronwright-Schreiner (1925), 'The normal profu-
sion of game over the inland flats of South Africa one hundred years
ago, or a little less, seems now incredible, but there is no doubt about
it. In addition to the overwhelming testimony of the South African

---

[4]The Grzimeks used a small plane—a method which has recently proved
most valuable—to observe, record and photograph the migrations of game
over the Serengeti plains.

farmers on the spot, many books of the early hunters from Great Britain (e.g. Cornwallis Harris, Gordon Cumming and others) dwell upon it with amazement. . . . In December 1880, just before my eighteenth birthday, I was at Kuilfontein near Coleberg. The owner, Mr. Murray, must have been born in about 1820 or perhaps a few years earlier. One day, standing with me near his house, he was telling me of the enormous numbers of game (not only springbucks) when first he knew Kuilfontein. Pointing to a low rand, some two or three miles away, he assured me that, in the mornings before driving his sheep out of the kraals (folds) to graze, he used often to send a "boy" (coloured servant) to drive the game off the proposed grazing ground under the rand'.

In the year 1848, George Nicholson wrote of the plains beyond the Orange River in the following terms: 'They are, in most cases, covered with game; in some places immense herds of springboks, thousands in numbers, are seen; in other places, they are intermingled with many troops of grotesque gnoos, and of the heavy-looking quaggas; elsewhere are ostriches, while numerous flocks of the beautiful Balearic cranes everywhere stalk about in search of insects and bulbs.

'The country here is not well enough supplied with water to permit of its being much inhabited by farmers. A few years ago it was much infested with lions, but now they are rarely seen, and then only during or after the emigrations of these vast herds of springboks which often pass over this country after a continuance of south-easterly winds, and cause the entire destruction of all the pasturage in their route.

'Some idea may be formed of the extent of this plague, when I assert that I have seen a column of these animals of at least fifteen miles in length, and so closely packed together in some places, that nine of them fell at one discharge from a large gun. These columns march on in unbroken masses, till they reach the high mountains which bound their native plains; in ascending these, they become dispersed by the nature of the ground, and then great havoc is committed among them by all in the neighbourhood who possess guns, and not a few become victims to the rapicity of the panthers and hyaenas inhabiting those regions'.

Finally, an extract from an incident described by T. B. Davie in Cronwright-Schreiner's book: 'From the year 1887 there were four really great treks over the Prieska District, three with a northern course, and one to the south and west. When the trek was in full move nothing but springbok were to be seen for miles upon miles at a stretch. The whole country seemed to move, not in any hurry or rush, as is generally associated in peoples' minds with a springbok, but a steady plodding march, just like "voetganger" (hopper) locusts; no other animal or insect life can afford so apt an illustration. The writer has seen them in one continuous stream, on the road and on both sides of the road, to the sky-line, from the town of Prieska to Draghoender, a distance of 47 miles, plodding on, just moving aside far enough to avoid the wheels of the cart.

'On this occasion the owners of the farm Witvlei were all sitting in a ring round the top of the well, which at that time was uncovered, the father, son and son-in-law armed with rifles, firing a shot now and then, and the womenfolk with sticks and stones trying to keep the "boks" away. This was the family's only water supply left, as the "boks" had already filled the dam, thousands being trampled to death in the mud as they pressed on over one another to get to the water. At last the "boks" beat the farmers and got to the well and in a few minutes it was full of dead and dying "boks".'

The significance of such migrations is but one of a number of problems, the answers to which we can now never learn.[5] Cronwright-Schreiner himself wrote that even in the intense heat and aridity of the Karoo and beyond, springbuck could go for long periods without water. In many regions thereabouts, farmers considered themselves fortunate if they got two or three storms in a year. He continued, 'It is true that springbucks are fleet of foot and might travel long distances to drink, if there were water; yet normally in my experience, they do not do so, nor do they seem to suffer from

[5]Another peculiarity of springbuck is the habit of jumping into the air and from which they get their name. Cronwright-Schreiner describes this as follows: 'The attitude of the pronking springbuck is very like that of a bucking horse. The head is lowered almost to the feet, the legs hang fully extended with the hoofs almost brushed together; this arches the back sharply and throws the haunches down, making the legs appear almost unduly long. In an instant the buck seems to spurn the earth as it shoots up into the air to an incredible height, perhaps straight up; for an instant it hangs arched, then down it drops. . . . The buck seems scarcely to touch the earth when it bounds up into the air again like a rocket, perhaps with a prodigious leap forward and as high as before; for a second you see it in the air, its mane up, its fan raised and opened in a sharp arch, the white patch blazing in the sun and the long hairs glittering, the legs and head all hanging in a bunch under the body; then it touches earth again, only to bound up once more at a sharp angle to one side, then straight up, then to the other side, then forward, and so it goes on'.

The probable explanation of this habit is that the buck lives on the open flats where its velt enemies, lions, leopards, lynxes, etc. are unable to catch it by speed, but must rely on lying in hiding, rushing and pouncing upon it. Sudden pronking is the buck's safeguard and even kids, only a day or two old, do it. In addition, such action affords warning to other members of the herd as it is so conspicuous and can be seen from afar.

The ability to leap an extraordinary distance is not confined to the springbuck. Fitzsimons (1919) tells how a klipspringer leapt 30 ft from the edge of a rocky precipice to a jutting ledge below. It steadied itself for a moment and then ran at a fast pace obliquely down the precipice.

this deprivation. F. C. Selous comments similarly on the gemsbok; the same comment is applicable to the ostrich. Trekking would not seem to be primarily in search of water; for instance the great trek of 1816 did not follow the Orange River, but struck into the dry parts. . . .'.

The Boers divided springbucks into two categories; 'hou-bokhen' which remained permanently in particular areas of the velt and 'trek-bokkers' which occupied less favourable country and were subject to the vast emigrations mentioned above. This suggests that food-shortage, coupled with an excess population increase, rather than drought, may have been the driving factor in springbuck migration—the view expressed by Walter Heape. Millais also suggested that the springbuck in the Bushmanland desert could live without water on dry food and succulent roots.

During their treks, the normal behaviour of the springbuck changes considerably. The animals become restless, wander aimlessly, are startled without cause and gallop off in any direction until they collect together again. Yet they lose their natural shyness and even, as we have seen, enter villages and towns. Changes of behaviour during migration, however, are a common occurrence amongst other kinds of animals and no real explanation of the phenomenon has yet been given.[6]

The last springbuck migration took place in South-West Africa in 1954. It was on a comparatively small scale.

Nomadism, a life of wandering, is common amongst the inhabitants of arid and semi-arid lands. When the vegetation is insufficient to support a permanent population, the inhabitants have to travel far from one feeding ground to another. When such nomadism is regularised by seasonal rainfall, it becomes true migration, involving an outward journey and a return journey. The subject has been discussed in great detail by Dr. Walter Heape in his book *Emigration, Migration and Nomadism* (1931), who points out that nomadic species frequently migrate to a special part of their territory to give birth to the young. Such movements occur in elephants, hippopotamuses, kudu and other antelope to mention only a few.

One of the driving forces in animal evolution is selection of the environment by the organism. This is achieved chiefly by nomadism and migration. It is a sobering thought that even by restricting animals to game reserves and national parks, we cannot help but affect the course of their evolution and thereby change them into something they would not otherwise be. Animals are physiologically and psychologically adapted to their particular ecological niches. Their senses, instincts and capacities for learning are all products of

[6]Cloudsley-Thompson, 1960.

natural selection in their own and their ancestors' environments. If we alter these environments in any way, we influence selection and thereby change the species living there. One does not know, for example, to what extent predation by lions and other carnivores may be necessary to maintain zebras and other herbivores as they occur in nature, but it is a fact that animals which have been reared in zoos differ morphologically and physiologically from their wild relatives. This is a direct effect of environmental change. Moreover, the animals that are most docile and breed most successfully in captivity are not necessarily those that would be most productive in the wild. Consequently an hereditary, genetic change will soon occur in a species whose environment has been altered. This may be preferable to exterminating it altogether and there is no other alternative, but we should be aware it is so.

Running the gauntlet. From W. M. Kerr (1887).

CHAPTER VI

REACTIONS OF BIG GAME TO MAN

IN 1898, Colonel J. H. Patterson was sent by the Foreign Office to supervise construction of a section of the railway that was being built from Mombasa to the interior of Uganda. Whilst he was stationed at Tsavo, two voracious and insatiable man-eating lions appeared upon the scene and, for over nine months, waged intermittent warfare against the railway workers, culminating in a perfect reign of terror when they succeeded in bringing work to a complete standstill for about three weeks. At first they were not always successful but, as time went on, they braved almost any danger in their efforts to obtain human victims. Lt.-Col. Patterson eventually succeeded in shooting them both, but not until they had managed to carry off and devour an almost incredible number of the railway workmen.

Of the many popular misconceptions about wild animals, few can be more widespread than those concerning their ferocity and aggressiveness. It is natural that isolated stories of man-eaters and narrow escapes should catch the imagination, but they give an exaggerated and erroneous impression, for few animals will normally attack a man unless molested or injured. One hears less often of the innumerable travellers who not only do not build thorn fences round their camps when in lion country, but actually allow their fires to die down with impunity!

Of course, it is possible too, to go to the opposite extreme. Visitors to the game parks of East Africa need to be reminded by large notices that 'Elephant have right of way'. Indeed, most wild species pay so little attention to people in cars that one gets the impression that they must be tame. So it is not so difficult to understand how a man was killed by an elephant not long ago when he got out of his car to offer it a bun.

Elephant

According to Major J. Stevenson-Hamilton (1912), the famous South African game warden and Director of National Parks, elephants present a curious mixture of timidity and aggression. Though the slightest odour of human beings is sometimes sufficient to scare them away from the neighbourhood, they will on occasion attack in an entirely unprovoked manner. At one time there existed, in the Nile Province of Uganda, a herd of several hundreds of animals, mostly cows and immature bulls, which became such a terror to wayfarers that the road near their haunts was shunned by travellers. Although left alone for some years the herd had previously received considerable attention from sportsmen and apparently cherished the memory of former grievances. Half a day's march to the north, the local elephants showed an entirely different disposition and betrayed no signs of truculence.

Captain J. H. Speke, the explorer, in his *Journal of the Discovery of the Source of the Nile* (1863) gives this account of the 'suffragette' herd which he met at Unyoro, Uganda on 2 September 1862 : 'On arrival at the end, we heard that elephants had been seen close by. Grant[1] and I then prepared our guns, and found a herd of about a hundred feeding on a plain of long grass, dotted here and there by small mounds crowned with shrub. The animals appeared to be all females, much smaller[2] than the Indian breed; yet, though ten were fired at, none were killed, and only one made an attempt to charge. I was with the little twin Manua at the time, when, stealing along under cover of the high grass, I got close to the batch and fired at the largest, which sent her round roaring. The whole of them then, greatly alarmed, packed together and began sniffing the air with their uplifted trunks, till, ascertaining by the smell of the powder that their enemy was in front of them, they rolled up their trunks and came to the spot where I was lying under a mound. My scent then striking across them, they pulled up short, lifted their heads high, and looked down sideways on us. This was a bad job. I could not get a proper front shot at the boss of any of them, and if I had waited an instant we should both have been picked up and trodden to death : so I let fly at their temples, and instead of killing sent the whole of them rushing away at a much faster pace than they came. After this I gave up, because I never could separate the ones I had wounded from the rest, and thought it cruel to go on damaging more'.

Of course, in one's sympathy for game, it is easy to overlook the fact that they at times can be a confounded nuisance. This is well illustrated by the following extracts from the diary of T. H. Parke: '12 December [1887]—I went out for a shot today, but got none. The Manyuema are constantly discharging their tower muskets, in order to frighten off elephants and other trespassers from their crops; this practice keeps all game at a respectful distance from us'.

'16 June [1888] The elephants are fast eating our bananas'.

[1]Captain James A. Grant, Speke's staunch comrade.
[2]Probably *Loxodonta africana cyclotis*—see p. 141. J. L. C-T.

Buffalo, Uganda

Giraffe, Kenya

Zebra, Amboseli, Kenya

Male wildebeest,
Ngorongoro,
Tanzania

'4 August—Last night a very large elephant came up to within twenty yards of the Fort, and ate a great quantity of our young Indian corn, which we had been congratulating and priding ourselves on having cultivated so successfully. . . . These elephants have now commenced tearing down trees, and eating up our bananas, in a quite systematic way. This is really serious for us, as, if allowed to go on in this fashion, we will, at the end of a few weeks, have neither bananas nor corn for the men to eat, and there is little chance of any other source of supply. So great a source of anxiety has it become, that our one great hope now is of the relief, which we are hoping and praying that Jephson and Emin Pasha may bring us'.

'24 November—The sentries heard an elephant moving about in the *chamba* (clearing), last night about twelve o'clock. They fired one shot, after which the animal moved off a few yards; but did not leave the place until the ivory alarm had been blown for about fifteen minutes. The brute could be distinctly heard breaking down branches and feeding, at a distance or two or three hundred yards. . . .'.

'25 November—One month separating us from Christmas—a bright lookout! Another holiday of starvation'.

Nevertheless, despite the anxiety he had been caused by them, Parke was still able to appreciate the great beasts. 'On the right bank of the Congo, opposite the junction of the Kassai river, large herds of elephants may be seen wandering about, enjoying the undisturbed quiet of the primeval forest. One group I saw, which contained at least one hundred splendidly developed specimens. The African elephant moves in his native haunts with a degree of nimbleness and agility which is quite astounding when seen for the first time by Europeans, whose previous experience of the animal has been derived from the commercial specimens of the menagerie, or those confined in the Zoological Gardens. I was not prepared for it'.

When not molested, elephants tend to ignore human beings and in Uganda I have seen African villagers walking within 100 yards of a herd of elephant, neither taking the slightest notice of the other. In the southern Sudan, accompanied by game scouts with bags of fine sand with which they constantly tested the direction of the wind, I was twice able to walk to within the same distance of herds of about 40 elephants. When we circled so that our scent reached them, they bunched together and moved off. It was a wonderful sight to see these magnificent creatures, with the ox-peckers on their backs, sweeping through the yellow grass. When they flapped their big ears, the dust flew from their flanks as though from a house-maid's mop. H. M. Stanley (1872) once had an unexpectedly close encounter with a large elephant which immediately fled: 'I strode up the bank', he wrote, 'and my astonishment may be conceived when I found myself directly in front of an elephant, who had his large broad ears held out like studding sails—the colossal monster, the incarnation of African world. . . .'. Stanley had a most irritating, flowing literary style which contrasts ill with the dramatic prose of Baker, Burton and Livingstone, but one sympathises with him when he castigates hunters for their extraordinary exaggerations. 'I have heard young officers on the Zanzibar coast, who were just past their teens, relating with an astonishing glibness and volubility the tremendous adventures they had had with elephants, leopards, lions, and what not. If they shot at a hippopotamus in the river, they had killed him; if they had met an antelope near the coast, it was almost sure to be a lion, and they had bowled him over; if they had seen an elephant in a zoological garden, it was sure to be told he had been met in Africa, and "bagged, sir, without any trouble; and I have the tusks at home now, which I can show, if you like, some day". It is a disease, a mania with some people, that they never can relate the positive, literal, exact truth. Travelling in Africa is adventurous enough as it is, without any fiction'.

D. Denham and H. Clapperton in their *Narrative of Travels and Discoveries in Northern and Central Africa* (1826) were clearly aware that elephants are normally comparatively inoffensive and try to avoid interference from man. 'The sheikh's people began screeching violently: and although at first they appeared to treat our approach with great contempt, yet after a little they moved off, erecting their ears, which had until then hung flat on their shoulders, and giving a roar that shook the ground under us. One was an immense fellow, I should suppose sixteen feet high: and the other two were females, and moved away rather quickly, while the male kept in the rear, as if to guard their retreat. We wheeled swiftly round him; and Maramy casting a spear at him, which struck him just under the tail, and seemed to give him about as much pain as when we prick our finger with a pin, the huge beast threw up his proboscis in the air with a loud roar, and from it cast such a volume of sand, that, unprepared as I was for such an event, nearly blinded me. The elephant rarely, if ever, attacks; and it is only when irritated that he is dangerous: but he will sometimes rush upon a man and horse, after choking them with dust, and destroy them in an instant'.

Major Henry Darley (1926) mentions that, in the only instance he knew personally of an elephant charging 'without rhyme or reason, it was covered with wounds from head to tail, which were suppurating and running down its sides. The animal had been shot all over, evidently by a band of Abyssinians, and the "Gras" rifle bullets were embedded just under the skin'. It was in such a dreadful state that even the natives would not eat it.

'By following the trail of elephants they can be found standing
asleep about noon—generally in the middle of the plain—and, by
approaching quietly, one can often get within twenty or thirty yards
without disturbing them.' This quotation, also from T. H. Parke
(1891), certainly does not give the impression of very dangerous
animals.

An aggressive young elephant was, however, met by the Duke
Adolphus Frederick of Mecklenburg on the Ituri river. Nevertheless,
as shown by the following passage from his book *In the Heart of
Africa* (1910), he did not incur any danger. 'The approach of the
boats appeared to arouse a certain amount of uneasiness amongst the
elephants, which was evinced by the raising of their trunks and the
flapping of their ears. Creating a tremendous ripple in the stream,
they returned to the bank, where there was a young animal who
appeared to be in a very aggressive mood, and who was venting his
spleen on the boughs of the trees, whilst the others stepped out of
their bath and crashed into the forest. The youngster raged around
for a time trumpeting, and then, turning in circles in the shallow
water near the bank, sucked up the water in his trunk and spurted
it into the air. As no danger appeared to threaten our boat, I dropped
my rifle and picked up my camera. Just then the ill-natured beast
took his departure !'

When Count G. Ahlefeldt Bille (1951) had shot a big bull elephant
that was winkled out of a herd of 200, the whole area suddenly
became a seething mass of stampeding elephants. Even so, none of
them came directly at him, although a herd of ten to fifteen, or
probably more, charged furiously past and uncomfortably near. Trees
snapped, bushes were swept down, and elephants screamed and
trumpeted all round; but the noise subsided towards the river, and
quiet was restored in a very short time.

Not always are elephants as docile when attacked as some writers
would have us think. E. M. Jack (1914) quotes an adventure experienced by his friend Capt. the Hon. F. R. D. Prittie near Fort Portal,
Uganda, who hoped to shoot one of a big herd of elephants that he
found. 'At last they began to move slowly across my front up wind
of my little hill. I left it and crept down to within fifty yards of the
nearest elephant and prayed that a big one who was just behind
might come to the edge of the herd. He did, and I got a very easy
shot at his heart at just the right angle. As usual he went about ten
steps and fell.

'The whole herd pushed off up wind with a yell, and so did Simba
[the gunbearer] and I in the other direction (but without wasting our
breath). They formed up absolutely shoulder to shoulder in line,
perfectly dressed, about three hundred yards off, and then came

straight back over the place where the dead one lay. There were over two hundred of them and the ground really did shake. The faithful Simba and myself were going like the wind, and just cleared their right flank comfortably. I wasn't too happy personally. I hate running in rather long grass with a heavy rifle, and I dislike the noise an elephant makes when he's cross.

'They didn't wait after their futile charge—nor did we—but broke up at once into small bodies, thirty or forty strong, and started cruising round looking for us. We just managed to keep the wind right but we had to go all out, and every time a posse of them crossed our track they stopped and yelled. We were both of us pretty done by the time we got out of the beaten zone. The elephants hunted for about half an hour or so and then pushed off southwards and we saw them no more'.

W. J. Burchell (1822) related how Carl Kruger, an indefatigable and fearless hunter as well as an excellent marksman, often ventured into the most dangerous situations. One day, 'having with his party pursued an elephant which he had wounded, the irritated animal suddenly turned round, and, singling out from the rest the person by whom he had been wounded, seized him with his trunk, and, lifting his wretched victim high in the air, dashed him with dreadful force to the ground. His companions, struck with horror, fled precipitately from the fatal scene, unable to turn their eyes to behold the rest of the tragedy. But on the following day they repaired to the spot, where they collected the few bones that could be found, and buried them near the spring. The enraged animal had not only trampled his body literally to pieces, but could not feel its vengeance satisfied till it had pounded the very flesh into the dust, so that nothing of this unfortunate man remained, excepting a few of the larger bones'.

Only a few years ago, an elephant near Kasungu in Malawe first killed two separate men; the evidence later showed that it had deliberately hunted and not just stumbled across them. Then it came upon a woman gathering firewood, carrying her baby on her back as usual, and accompanied by a small boy. The elephant first disposed of the boy with one sweep of its trunk and then attacked the woman by bashing her and her baby with the bundle of firewood she had put together, opening up her abdomen. The woman pushed back the intestines and somehow managed to get back to the village but both mother and child died. The elephant walked on past the chief's office and found at a waterhole a woman whom it killed. By this time men with rifles had been summoned and the elephant was shot. When killed, it proved to have a festering sore on its rump from an old bullet wound, which explained its behaviour.[3]

[3]Debenham, 1955.

An elephant can attack in two different ways: either he will choose a rapid pace (a speed of about ten miles an hour) or he will charge. It is therefore impossible to know from his speed whether or not attack is intended. Occasionally a wounded elephant will hunt a man down most scientifically, circling round until he scents him and then charging. On the other hand, elephants that apparently charge from a distance will often turn aside at the last moment, proving that an attack was not intended.

W. D. M. Bell always insisted that the majority of so-called charges are no more than head-long flights in the wrong direction. Often elephants come towards a hunter because they cannot distinguish a motionless figure and depend almost entirely on smell or movement. This is fortunate, because a really angry elephant of large size is a terror to all within a hundred yards or so. It is very difficult to shoot him in the brain as his head is constantly in violent agitation. He swirls round as if on a ball-bearing and is a demon to avoid as he rushes furiously forward or backward, thrashing the bush on all sides, his trunk seeming to reach everywhere.

When a bull elephant becomes old and loses his status within the family circle, he may remain for a while with the group but eventually he is expelled and becomes a 'rogue'. According to Heinrich Oberjohann (1953) these old elephants are really quite peaceful. Sometimes he would try to provoke them by jumping out and blocking their path at a distance of about fifteen yards. At this they would stand rigid and motionless for about ten seconds before responding with a deep, angry trumpeting accompanied by an involuntary tremor of the head. If he countered with a sudden yell and feint attack, the old elephants would hold their ground up to twenty feet, then bolt as if the devil were at their heels.

It seems to be generally agreed that cows and immature males are more dangerous than old bulls and Bell describes a genuine charge from a cow elephant after he had shot one or two bulls in the herd. He could not at first believe that she meant business, but every time he moved she came at him, bristling with fury. Eventually he shot her and, on inspection, found that her newly born calf had been trampled to death in the commotion following his earlier shots. Edouard Foá (1899) also pointed out that one must always beware of female elephants that are feeding their young, especially females without tusks, because they charge almost always and sometimes without any more provocation than a shout or the report of a rifle.

An example of how aggressive an elephant can be after it has been wounded is given by Sir Samuel Baker (1866): 'For a moment he fell upon his knees, but, recovering with wonderful quickness, he was in full charge upon me. Fortunately I had inspected my ground previous to the attack and away I went up the inclination to my right, the spurs hard at work and the elephant screaming with rage, *gaining* on me. My horse felt as though made of wood, and clumsily rolled along in a sort of cow-gallop—in vain I dug the spurs into his flanks, and urged him by rein and voice: not an extra stride could I get out of him, and he reeled along as though thoroughly exhausted, plunging in and out of the buffalo holes instead of jumping them. . . . I kept looking round, thinking that the elephant would give in: we had been running for nearly half a mile, and the brute was over-hauling me so fast that he was within ten or twelve yards of the horse's tail, with his trunk stretched out to catch him. Screaming like the whistle of an engine, he fortunately so frightened the horse that he went his best, although badly, and I turned him suddenly down the hill and doubled back like a hare. The elephant turned up the hill, and entering the jungle, he relinquished the chase, when another hundred yard's run would have bagged me. In a life's experience in elephant-hunting, I never was hunted for such a distance'. (p. 137.)

Throughout this book I would have liked to have avoided stories of aggressive behaviour on the part of animals wounded or irritated by man, as the normal reactions of game are of greater zoological interest. When left to themselves, however, wild animals usually avoid or ignore man whilst the majority of men take pains to molest and kill wild game. I have therefore had to include some hunting stories and have selected ones that are unusually exciting. This section is concluded with a quotation from a book by Capt. C. A. Sykes (1903) which gives a fine impression of elephant tenacity.

'I was sauntering along somewhat unconcernedly, and getting bored, as one is apt to after the fifteenth mile, when my eyes chanced to rest upon what at first seemed to me to be a conglomeration of rocks, or a small village. I took out my glasses, wondering whose village it might be, and saw to my astonishment that what I had taken to be huts was actually moving. At the same time, Bazruta stopped dead, and uttered his customary exclamation, "hist", which he did when anything unusual came into his vision. With his quick eye he saw at once what it was, and whispered "fil". It then dawned upon me that ahead of me was standing a closely packed herd of elephants.

'I stopped the caravan and made it lie down, and, accompanied by my orderly and one other retainer, I made a bee-line for the herd. My recent success had given me confidence, and I approached without a trace of the nervousness that had seized me during my first adventure. The breeze came straight from the direction of the elephants—which were having their usual midday siesta—and everything seemed propitious. The ground was rocky, and covered with high grass, there being only a few short fig trees scattered here and there: the elephants had for some reason chosen the open ground to sleep in, unprotected from the direct rays of the sun. This is rather unusual, for their skins are extraordinarily sensitive, and they much prefer the shade of a tree if it is to be found. When I drew near I waited still for a few moments to thoroughly inspect the beasts. There were between forty and fifty of them, and they were all touching each other—indeed, so closely packed were they that a man could not have made his way through them. With my glasses I searched through all their tusks to find the largest of them, and ascertained that the finest pair was right in the centre. I tried to place myself so that I could get a shot at some vital spot, but wherever I tried, the great beast seemed to be covered, as if by design. I was soon within ten yards of them, and they still seemed unaware of our proximity. All at once the breeze slightly shifted, and our scent must have awakened them, for they seemed to detect the presence of some danger, and became uneasy. For about a second they moved about, and then without any warning went off as if by a word of command, simultaneously and without losing their relative positions. They passed within a few yards of me, and I could almost have stroked one of them. As they moved away, the big one exposed his quarters to me, and fearing that I should lose them from my supineness, I determined to risk a shot. Anything more reckless or stupid can hardly be imagined by a hunter of any experience! I knew that the elephant is vulnerable in the spine, and thinking I might hit him there, I bent low and fired upwards at his tail at an angle of about 45°. Such a deed was simple madness, for I had not a big rifle to fall back upon, and it emanated from my crass ignorance. Looking back upon it now, I can hardly conceive what I expected to happen! I know now that my chance of dropping the elephant was remote, and that the chance of his turning upon me was very much the reverse!

'The bullet went home, and must have inflicted a most painful wound, for the beast went on, using his hind legs wide apart, whisking his tail violently, with the blood pouring out as if a tap had been turned on. He did not seem disposed to anger at first, but only anxious to remain in the midst of the herd. The latter was obviously much disturbed by the crack of the rifle and the smack of the bullet as it struck. A few cows and young ones detached themselves and wandered off to the right, stepping up high and elevating their trunks in an absurd manner. The others ambled on straight, and getting amongst a few fig trees, they stopped for a short time to feed, ripping some of the branches down almost to the ground. I followed on! My orderly implored me to desist, and urged that he had elephant hunted in Emin's day, and that he knew these were battāl, or bad, from their very appearance. But my conceit must have been as hopeless as my ignorance, for I told him I had not expected fear in him. Seeing that I was bent upon continuing the chase, he had not the heart to leave me, and I suppose meant to make the best of a bad job. He also saw that another unfortunate retainer, who was armed with a Martini-Henry, kept with us. This rifle might certainly have been of the last importance.

'After about another mile we came up with the herd again. I noticed that they had re-formed themselves as before, the paterfamilias in the middle, and the smaller ones round him with their heads rather inclined outwards. This time I was not going to waste my time any more upon the big one, and resting my .303 upon the branch of a bush, I aimed at the brain of the nearest one—an average tusker. I fired, and distinctly heard the thud of the bullet as it entered his head. I must have been a trifle low, or the animal must have slightly shifted his head at the critical moment, for he did not fall. On the other hand he turned suddenly in my direction, opened his mouth and trumpeted. For a beast of such vast size the voice is ridiculous, and is similar to the sound of a penny trumpet: but for all its small-ness, I can conceive nothing more terrifying. It made the blood run cold in my veins, and I devoutly wished I had never fired that shot. I was only ten paces off, and saw distinctly the angry gleam in his eye as he charged. The further disturbance of my second shot had infuriated the rest of the herd, and headed by the other wounded one, who was now roused to an awful passion, they all trumpeted and joined in the hunt.

'Yes! The hunt had changed. My two poor companions and I were the quarry, and we were being hunted! The second retainer was terror-stricken. He shouted out for us to separate so that only one might be killed; but Bazruta pointed his rifle at him, and said he was to remain with him, between the commandant and the elephants, and that the first to be killed must be one of them. I must say I have often felt sorry for that second man: he never wanted to be there in the first place, and when he was there he was not allowed to escape in his own way! Bazruta behaved with the most magnificent devotion, and kept his presence of mind admirably throughout a trying twenty minutes. There was nothing for it but to run, and run we did. I have never in my life run like it before or since—but then I have never been in such a fright! With a start of ten yards, what chance had three bipeds on their legs, with animals that can keep pace with a mounted man? Moreover, the going was atrocious, and we kept stumbling at every step over rocks and boulders, and unevennesses of the ground. However, there were two things in our favour, or I should not now be relating this story! One was the fact that we soon got into a hollow, where there was no breeze, and scarcely any scent, and, secondly, the natural short-sightedness of our pursuers.

'Bending low down so that we were almost invisible in the long grass, we suddenly doubled to the right. This had the effect of confusing and delaying the creatures. They must have taken some little time casting about, for we undoubtedly gained about fifty yards. On we went, blinded with sweat and struggling for dear life. I felt that this unequal race could only end one way, and went through all the agonies of the poor hunted fox—and I inwardly vowed that I would never hunt him again. Every minute seemed to bring the huge brutes nearer, and I awaited the tap on the shoulder, which would end matters. Gradually it dawned upon me that I was becoming exhausted and, could not last much longer. It would not have availed to fling ourselves to the ground—the last refuge of a man when charged by a single elephant—for how could we expect a whole herd to pass us by? But the love of life is very powerful, and strengthens the sinews! We dashed on; but our tormentors were coming up to us again and my heart sank. Now did I fully realise my folly in firing at all, and my madness in not abandoning the chase when my orderly had warned me!

'At this desperate juncture we suddenly came upon a nullah. Bazruta was just behind, calm and collected, scorning to leave me, which, with his activity, he might easily have done, and called to me to jump down. I cared not if I was leaping into a bottomless pit— anything to escape from the present pressing danger—I jumped!

'As it chanced, it was not more than ten feet down, and though we were cut and bruised, we picked ourselves up and ran along the bottom with what seemed a new lease of life. To my great joy, the rent in the ground was narrow, and the consciousness of the fact that the elephant cannot jump, and that he does not care to descend into any narrow place, was most refreshing. After covering another hundred and fifty yards, Bazruta climbed up again and peeped over the grass. To my intense relief he said the elephants had lost the scent, and were snuffing about at the edge of the nullah. I asked where the escort was, for amongst them was safety, and I was told they were far off. But some instinct told me my faithful orderly was wrong, and I seemed to guess the direction. We now moved at a walk to try and recover ourselves, having a fairly good start. But they came on again, and the brief respite to my nerves was gone. My efforts were becoming frantic, my hat blew off—which Bazruta returned for and recovered. I asked afterwards why he had done such a thing, and he imperturbably said that he knew the white man gets sunstroke without his hat, and that I should then have fallen a victim to the elephants. On we went, and at last my instinct proved to be true, for we came quite suddenly upon the caravan and escort who had moved on, instead of remaining where we had left them as the orderly thought. I fell in the Somalis, who formed the escort, at once, and gave the words: "Ready! Present!"

'Whether it was the gleam of the rifles or the presence of a big caravan, I cannot say, but the two wounded elephants, who were now leading the herd, suddenly swerved off. This created a panic amongst the rest, and they all turned tail and fled; closely packed as before, with the two wounded ones behind. I watched them disappearing with as much joy as earlier I had watched them getting closer. I had been through both sides of a hunt, and never want to again. The two injured ones, as I watched, kept losing ground, and were evidently sorely hurt. At last, over an undulation of the ground, they passed out of our sight, which made me feel quite five years younger.

'As the reaction set in I felt completely exhausted, and was not invigorated by the remembrance that I had another five miles to walk before reaching camp. I lay on the ground, trembling from my exertions, and the porters came and poured water over me. I let it soak through my clothes and hair—it was delicious!'

Rhinoceros

The black rhinoceros has a reputation amongst some people for being a malicious monster, eager to attack every human being he meets. Others consider his charge to be merely a hasty and ill-considered attempt at all costs to get away from danger. In a recent study, A. T. A. Ritchie[4] suggests that rhinos can be divided very approximately into three groups according to temperament. The first contains rhinos in areas where they have for many years been hunted by natives using poisoned arrows. The result is a race of truculent animals whose survival lies in offensive action. Flight results in an arrow flicked into the flanks whilst a charge sends the hunter frantically diving for his life through a thorn bush and gives him no chance of using his bow.

The second group contains rhinos which dwell in open plains sparsely populated by pastoral tribes such as the Masai. Here rhinos are undisturbed by man unless, as rarely happens, some individual beast, in a fit of temper, charges cattle or the women at a water-hole, when he is promptly speared. A race of peaceable animals has thus grown up, always ready to retire unless provoked beyond endurance.

These are the extreme types of rhinoceros disposition. In between

[4](1963) E. Afr. Wildl. J. 1, 54-62.

lies a host of intermediates. Some are moderately even-tempered, some irritable, some are brave and others timid. Among these, the individual temperament of a rhino will, at any moment, play a part in deciding his action. Various conditions make for trouble, while others reduce the risk. For instance a cow with a calf will seldom charge home unless you are very close to her. The majority of rhinos in the third group will charge if they see a person before they hear him and are less likely to attack if they hear him first. Even so, they will not usually press home a charge unless they get too involved to withdraw. A shout or a shot into the ground will often turn them aside and a rhino that has charged and missed will seldom return to hunt for its objective.

The black rhinoceros is said to have three characteristic cries: a succession of deep grunts, uttered by the male alone and at certain seasons; a loud snort, sounded when the animal is about to charge or when suddenly alarmed; and the shrill squeal of a moribund individual.[5]

Lieut. Ludwig von Höhnel (1894) accompanied Count Samuel Teleki on his journeys in Eastern Equatorial Africa, during which Lakes Rudolf and Stefanie were discovered. On one occasion, he was following 'buffalo spoors' when he 'surprised a rhinoceros and very nearly had a mishap with him. We had only just noticed an ominous grunting in the thick bushes on our right, when crash went some branches, and a huge brownish-black beast dashed out with such tremendous impetus that I had only just time to step backwards into the bush and avoid the charge. I saw my two men fleeing before the lowered head of the rhinoceros, then I lost sight of them and all was still. In the greatest anxiety, I shouted to them, and to my delighted relief they both answered. Simba had with great presence of mind turned aside into the bush, and though he was a good deal scratched, he escaped. The other man had been in no real danger, but in his fright he had flung away my rifle, and we found it afterwards with both barrels stopped up with earth. We were a good bit upset by the surprise, and went on cautiously enough after this, expecting to see some huge beast behind every bush'.

According to Baker (1890), the black rhinoceros will attack man or beast, frequently without the slightest provocation. 'It is especially likely to attack should it obtain the wind (scent) of any person or strange animal before it appears in sight. This makes it extremely dangerous when riding through thick jungle or high grass, should a rhinoceros be somewhere concealed to leeward. I have myself been hunted out of the jungle by two rhinoceroses which thus gained our

[5]Lydekker, 1926.

wind, just as we had become aware of their existence through the presence of fresh droppings'.

On one occasion, W. A. Chanler (1896) had a narrow escape from a rhinoceros whilst he was stalking a small herd of zebra and two giraffes. 'While so engaged I noticed to my right, at a distance of about 200 yards, a solitary rhinoceros placidly feeding. We had sufficient rhinoceros meat so I did not disturb him. The wind was blowing from where I stood toward him, in short and irregular puffs. I had approached to within 200 yards of my quarry and was about to take aim, when a shrill whistle from my men reached my ears. I turned round, and just in time, for the rhinoceros upon scenting me at once made for me. The soft soil had deadened the sound of his approach. . . .'. Chanler managed to leap aside just in time to avoid the rush of the animal. He added: 'As a rule the rhinoceros snorts when it charges; but this one had not made a sound. Needless to say, I failed to get a shot at either the zebras or giraffes. However, while the men were pitching camp, they were charged by another rhinoceros, which paid the death penalty for its temerity. . . .'.

Lt.-Col. J. H. Patterson (1909) recorded a number of instances of rhinos charging people and even railway trains, without provocation. He mentioned that he had been chased on horseback many times by rhino, but only once was a really determined and persistent attack made.

No doubt the rhinoceros is dangerous, but far too many are shot in self-defence, either through carelessness or because, perhaps unconsciously, they have been provoked. And even then, provided one keeps cool, it is usually possible to avoid shooting. The rhinoceros has poor sight and is guided mainly by his sense of smell. Often he will not repeat the charge, but will simply run by, snorting and rather terrifying, with his tail up, following his nose. But he can turn on a sixpence, and has an astonishing gift for always being in a bad temper. One must be always on the alert and prepared for anything.[6]

The white rhinoceros is normally less aggressive than the black but, if suddenly disturbed, either species will come straight towards the aggressor. If the latter gets quickly out of the way, however, the rhino will usually rush straight on. On one occasion my wife and I walked to within fourteen paces of a pair of white rhinos sleeping peacefully under a tree. As we approached, they lumbered to their feet. One made off, but the other charged towards us. At a shout, however, it turned off into the long grass. No doubt the majority of such sudden charges are induced more by alarm coupled with poor vision and stupidity than with natural ferocity.

[6]Ahlefeldt Bille, 1951.

Hippopotamus

A hippo may sometimes charge if it finds its line of retreat to the water has been barred. An example of such an incident, which took place in Ethiopia, is given by E. A. de Cosson (1877). 'After again wading through the Arno Garno, we crept among the mimosa trees, our Witos leading the way with their long spears in their hand, as they said that if there were any *goumarie* (hippos) about they would perceive them long before we should. But we had hardly walked a hundred yards, when suddenly there was a cracking of branches, the trees in front of us parted asunder, and a huge black mass appeared rushing down upon us with short angry snorts, like a railway engine letting off steam. Out native hunters had got, without perceiving it, between the wind and a hippopotamus that was grazing on land, and which, finding its retreat to the lake cut off, had made up its mind to charge. The attack was so sudden that we found ourselves running as hard as we could before we well knew what we were running for; and the valiant Witos, who had been the first to turn, passed us like lightning and never stopped till they reached the river'.

A wicked hippo. From E. A. de Cosson (1877).

Of the hippopotamus, Sir Samuel Baker (1890) wrote: 'There is no animal that I dislike more, if I am compelled to travel at night upon an African river in an ordinary boat. There is no possibility of escape should a hippo take the idea into his head that your vessel is his enemy. The creature's snort may be heard at a few yards distance in the darkness, and the next moment you may be overturned by an attack from beneath, where the enemy was unseen. . . . All of my boats were more or less damaged by hippopotami in the course of three years' work upon the upper Nile. . . . In broad daylight a hippo charged the steamer that was towing my diabeeah. Not content with breaking several floats off the paddle-wheel, it reappeared astern, and, striking the bottom of our iron vessel, it perforated the plates in two with its projecting tusks, causing a dangerous leak.

'The most ferocious attack that I have ever witnessed occurred in the Bahr Giraffe, at a time when we were cutting a passage for the flotilla of fifty-seven vessels through the obstruction caused by aquatic vegetation, which had accumulated to an extent that blocked the navigation of the river. During the middle of the night a bull hippopotamus charged our diabeeah, and sank a small boat that was fastened to the side. The infuriated beast then bit the side out of a boat that was 17 feet in length, and the splash of splintered wood betokened its destruction. . . . Not satisfied with this success, it then charged the iron vessel, and would assuredly have sunk her if I had not stopped the onset by a shot in the skull. . . .'.

Col. C. Chaillé Long (1876) too, found hippos and crocodiles a menace. In his journal for 17 May 1874 he wrote: 'The river is filled with hippopotami and crocodiles; the former in undisturbed possession seemed to dispute our passage, by their uncomfortable proximity and fearful roars; the latter were still more dangerous. Not a day passed but that some too venturesome native was seized in or near the river'. Was this truth or exaggeration? We shall discuss the crocodile later (p. 177).

No doubt, as A. St H. Gibbons (1904) suggested, hippos and crocodiles may occasionally be an unfortunate combination. The Nile crocodile is a larger animal than his relative of the Zambesi; on the other hand, the hippopotamus, of which there are many in both rivers is smaller in the north than in the south. Both animals, he said, are dangerous, and instances of attacks on boats by the latter frequently occurred. He was told of one in which a canoe containing eight natives was overturned at Fajou by hippopotami, the whole crew falling victims to the appetite of countless crocodiles before any could reach the banks! I am quite sure that this was a gross exaggeration.

When R. C. F. Maugham first arrived in Zambesia in 1893, he heard many stories of the danger hippopotamuses were to small boats and canoes. 'For some hitherto unexplained reason, they are addicted to the playful habit of upsetting these frail craft, apparently for the pure enjoyment of watching the struggles of the occupants in the water. It is a curious fact that there are very few cases on record of the natives being molested whilst swimming, although this has happened. Having caused the capsize, the great beast does not retreat. He remains on the surface calmly regarding the catastrophe with an air of deprecating surprise which is almost apologetic'.

The following are typical accounts of unprovoked attacks by hippopotamus on small boats:

'Towards evening, while we were making but very slight way up the sluggish stream, a violent rush in the water, and the cries of the men—"A hippopotamus! a hippo!" caused me to seize my rifle and bound from my cabin on deck. The brute had just dived, passing within a yard of the boat, and a bang and a crack announced the staving in of the small boat in our wake, and the rupture of the rope by which it was attached. Half-a-dozen of the crew, unbidden, leaped into the stream and were up with the boat when gunwale deep in the water; they found its occupants, a few sheep, swimming about in it. Conducting it to the shore, we also made fast, when, hauling up our little craft we discovered a hole a foot square in its bows'.[7]

Elsewhere, the same author writes: 'The attacks on our boats by the hippopotami were as ridiculous as they were exhilarating. Upon one occasion, no less than five huge monsters beset us at once; and, raising their ungainly bodies half-way out of the water, attempted to board us, whilst, their capacious jaws extended to the utmost, they were actually terrifying. No end of bullets were fired into them by myself and the men. . . .'.

David and Charles Livingstone (1865) wrote that their canoe-men were afraid to venture among a herd of hippopotamus, 'because as they affirm, there is commonly an illnatured one in a herd, which takes a malignant pleasure in upsetting canoes'. 'While crossing the river [Zambesi] prior to forming a camp, an incident occurred which might have been unpleasant in its consequences. When about midstream the canoe which carried the bulk of my equipment was about four yards to my right. Suddenly, without any provocation, a hippopotamus rose in a deliberate attempt to overturn it, but fortunately the brute had not been very exact in his calculations for carrying out his ill-natured designs. His body merely struck the side of the canoe, which, after shipping a few quarts of water, regained its stability and was paddled rapidly ashore'.[8]

Some years ago in the Bahr el-Ghazal, Sudan, these animals overturned a felucca containing mails, twice in a month, and 'it was found necessary to issue permission to shoot at them from the steamer or boats. In this manner, of course, great numbers have been killed

[7]Petherick, 1861.
[8]Gibbons, 1904.

outright, or have subsequently died of their wounds, but the rivers to the south are still well stocked, and as long as they are not allowed to constitute an actual danger to life and property, it is to be hoped that they will be preserved. . . .'.[9]

Cow hippos, not unnaturally, are inclined to be vicious about calving time when they sometimes attack canoes and boats, perhaps regarding them as rivals. Old bulls, too, not infrequently act in the same way. Although occasionally stupidly ferocious in the water, a bull hippo, if disturbed on land, will immediately rush for safety. Probably most incidents occur from animals accidentally or in play rising beneath a boat and capsizing it. Except when wounded, it is rare for a hippopotamus having acted thus actually to pursue human beings in the water.

Lion

The risk of serious casualties in hunting elephants, buffaloes and rhinoceroses on foot is probably small compared with that of hunting lions. E. A. Temple-Perkins (1955) considers them the most dangerous of all African game animals (an opinion shared by Sir Alfred Pease) on account of their speed, agility and determination. They are sometimes said to be cowardly, yet few lions will shirk an encounter if it seems necessary. Like the Tsavo man-eaters, they have been known to board railway trains at night and take men out of the windows of carriages or to leap into crowded villages among the blazing watch-fires to seize their victims under a hail of flaming brands, spears and clubs, amid the yells of men and screeching of the women. They will even challenge in mortal combat such beasts as buffaloes, animals vastly superior in size and weight, well armed and ferocious.

Sir Samuel Baker once discovered the dislocated skeleton of a buffalo intermingled with the broken bones of a lion, the skull of which was lying nearby. The ground had been deeply trampled showing the desperate character of the recent struggle which had terminated in the death of both contestants. Probably two lions had attacked the buffalo which was killed after having vanquished one of its assailants. It is said that buffalo are hunted by lions only in certain parts of Africa where the art of tackling them is handed down from old to young by imitation.

On one occasion F. C. Selous (1893) rode up to within 100 yards of a pair of lions as they stood defiant. He turned his horse's head so as to pass them at a distance of 60-70 yards when 'the dark-maned lion came slowly towards me for a few steps, and then, bounding forward, and growling loudly, charged out at his best speed. As I had to half turn my horse and get him into his stride, the lion got to within some

[9]Fothergill, 1910.

ten yards or so of his tail before he was going at his best pace, and
stuck close to him for some distance. How far he chased me I am
afraid to say, but a very considerable distance, and certainly twice
as far as I have ever been pursued by any other of his kind'.

Selous concluded, that it is impossible to gauge the probable
behaviour of any dangerous animal by drawing conclusions from
the attitude previously shown by a single beast of the same species.
Sir Alfred Pease (1913), however, recorded a similar event that befell
one of his neighbours, Mr. Philip Percival. Percival was riding alone,
not far from the Kapiti Plains Railway Station in Kenya when, to
his surprise, his horse, aptly named 'Weary', began to trot. 'Trying
to account for this quite unprecedented exhibition of vitality, he
turned his head to see if there were any after cause—to his horror, he
saw a great lion coursing right for him, and drawing on at the awful
pace a lion can; at this particular moment the lion was some 40 yards
behind, in another second he would be at him—in went the spurs
and away "Weary" went, with death at his heels, as he never went
before; but the start was not enough, a few moments more and the
lion's great head came forging up to "Weary's" quarters. There had
been, of course, no chance or time to shoot and at this instant, in this
terrible race for life, it was still impossible. . . . Percival, believing that
his last minute had come, sent forth, he declares, the most piercing
yell that ever issued from human throat. The lion was so astonished
at this very unusual note that he forthwith pulled straight up, and
stared with astonishment. . . . This gave "Weary" a chance to pull
away and eventually the lion gave up the chase'.

W. D. M. Bell (1960) makes an interesting observation on lion
psychology: 'It has always seemed to me that lions may be placed
in two categories—those which kill their game, and those which
feed largely on carrion. Carrion feeding seems to be due chiefly to
old age or broken teeth. Most of those lions in robust health scarcely
ever touch carrion. The former are much bolder and more courageous
than the latter. At night they will attack strong zeribas containing
cattle in spite of shouts and firearms. When these take to man-eating
they do so most thoroughly, as instance the well-known cases of the
man-eaters of Tsavo. . . .'.

There can be no doubt that lions can be extremely dangerous, and
the risk is greatly magnified when they are molested. 'As East Africa
—Kenya—became better known sportsmen came in great numbers
for the shooting, and many lions were killed. As might be expected
these sportsmen included many who were mere novices at the game,
and who had little or no skill or experience in shooting, and as a
result it was attended by many casualties. In one year, out of forty
visiting sportsmen who devoted themselves seriously to lion hunting,

twenty were mauled. Of these twenty over half were killed or died of their wounds. The lions of this period were extraordinarily bold and courageous. In early morning in those huge plains I have walked steadily towards a troupe of lions numbering over a score, and just as steadily they walked away with no fear of man'.[10]

A curious lion story is told by E. A. de Cosson (1877) who heard it from a young Frenchman living in Ethiopia. The latter had 'gone out shooting pigs one day, with an old single-barrelled fowling-piece; and not finding any sport, had penetrated far into the forest, when towards sunset he came on some boar tracks which led him to a deep pool surrounded by rocks and big trees. On looking cautiously round one of these, he suddenly found himself face to face with three lions who were drinking the water. As he had only buck shot with him, it may be imagined that he retraced his steps again with the utmost rapidity and caution. At last he gained the open country, and was walking quietly along with his gun over his shoulder, whistling a tune, when he noticed two Shohos sitting under a tree, who the moment they caught sight of him flung their arms into the air and ran away as fast as they could. This conduct surprised him, and he glanced round to see what was the matter, when, lo and behold ! there were the three lions following him, in a grave and dignified manner, at about thirty yards' distance'.

According to Sir Richard Burton (1856), the Somalis have a 'superstition that the king of beasts will not attack a single traveller, because such a person, they say, slew the mother of all lions; except in darkness or during violent storms, which excite the fierce carnivores, he is a timid animal, much less feared by the people than the angry and agile leopard. Unable to run with rapidity when pressed by hunger, he pursues a party of travellers as stealthily as a cat, and arrived within distance, springs, strikes down the hindermost, and carries him away to the bush'.

F. L. James (1883) described an incident that befell two officers of the 'Blues' in the Khor Baraka at Gangi, near Tokar, Sudan. 'After having been asleep about two hours in the sandy bed of the khor, they were suddenly aroused from their slumbers by a horrible shriek and loud cries of "Asad, asad!" (lion). In a moment everyone was in a commotion, including the watchman, who had allowed all the fires but one to go out. . . . It soon appeared that it was not a sheep or a goat that had been carried off, but one of the natives who had been asleep by the fire. The lion had seized the poor fellow by the feet and dragged him for about four yards, and then left him, disturbed no doubt by the man's own shrieks and the shouts of his companions; and thanks also to the plucky and determined manner in which his

[10]Bell, 1960.

neighbour had held on to him. The unfortunate man had both feet severely injured by the lion's teeth, the greater part of the sole of each being torn away, leaving the bones, however, intact. He had little faith in the European method of curing his wounds, and insisted on carrying out his own method of treatment; this consisted in covering his wounds with wood-ashes, and placing the soles of his feet as near as possible to the fire'.

On one occasion, when on the railway to Nairobi, Major C. H. Stigand heard that lions had been coming to drink under a water-tank at Simba station, so he got leave to stop and sit up there. The lions came and he hit three. One of them was only wounded so he followed it in the dark when it sprang at him, knocked him down and gripped his left wrist. When he punched it, it left. Its lower jaw had been broken by a bullet which is presumably why Stigand was not killed.

Dr. David Livingstone (1857) was attacked by a lion that he had shot at near Kuruman in Bechuanaland. He stopped to reload but, 'When in the act of ramming down the bullets I heard a shout. Starting, and looking half round, I saw the lion just in the act of springing upon me. I was upon a little height; he caught my shoulder as he sprang, and we both came to the ground below together. Growling horribly close to my ear, he shook me as a terrier does a rat. The shock produced a stupor similar to that which seems to be felt by a mouse after the first shake by the cat. It caused a sort of dreaminess, in which there was no sense of pain nor feeling of terror, though quite conscious of all that was happening. It was like what patients partially under the influence of chloroform describe, who see all the operation, but feel not the knife. This singular condition was not the result of any mental process. The shake annihilated fear, and allowed no sense of horror in looking round at the beast. This peculiar state is probably produced in all animals killed by the carnivora; and if so, is a merciful provision by our benevolent creator for lessening the pain of death. Turning round to relieve myself of the weight, as he had one paw on the back of my head, I saw his eyes directed to Mababwe, who was trying to shoot him at a distance of ten or fifteen yards. His gun, a flint one, missed fire in both barrels; the lion immediately left me, and, attacking Mababwe, bit his thigh. Another man, whose life I had saved before, after he had been tossed by a buffalo, attempted to spear the lion while he was biting Mababwe. He left Mababwe and caught this man by the shoulder, but at that moment the bullets he had received took effect, and he fell down dead. The whole was the work of a few moments, and must have been its paroxysm of dying rage. In order to take out the charm from him, the Bakatla on the following day made a huge bonfire over the carcass, which was declared to be that of the largest lion they had ever seen. Besides crunching the bone into splinters, he left eleven teeth wounds in the upper part of my arm'. (p. 150.)

On the other hand, Petrus Jacobs, an old Boer hunter, who probably shot as many lions as any man, was once terribly mauled by one after he had shot at and missed it whilst it was stalking his horses. Years afterwards, he told F. C. Selous (1881) that the wounds often gave him great pain, especially in damp weather. Selous added: 'Remembering Dr. Livingstone's statement that when he was bitten by a lion he felt no sensation of pain, I asked Jacobs whether this was his case; but he emphatically denied it, saying that each scrunch gave him the most acute anguish. I believe, however, that most people who have been bitten by a lion or a tiger, agree with Dr. Livingstone, and imagine that the shock to the nervous system caused by the bite of one of these powerful animals is usually sufficient to deaden all sensation of pain for the time being'. H. Wolhunter, as related on pp. 159-60, also felt extreme pain when bitten by a lion.

Pease (1913) quotes Mr. H. Williams who was attacked by a lion in Kenya during June 1909, after he had wounded it: 'It was a terrifying sight—the brute's jaws already open to seize me by the left shoulder and breast—but with the courage born of despair I raised my rifle in both hands and struck him across the side of the head. Almost simultaneously he ducked and seized me by the right leg, shaking me from side to side as though I had been a rat. There is no need to describe what I felt at this moment. . . .'. Williams was saved through the courage of his gunbearer who first came up and asked him how to turn the safety catch of the rifle he was carrying. It is interesting that, in this account, pain is not mentioned until an hour after the wounds were made.

It is certainly true that, at moments of extreme danger one does not feel pain or fear, probably because one is far too much taken up with the situation. On one occasion during the Second World War, when suddenly faced by a German Super Tiger tank at a range of 35 yards, the thought crossed my mind that I was certainly going to be killed; for I was in a British Cromwell tank whose 75 mm shots just bounced off the massive armour of the enemy. But I did not begin to feel frightened until a few seconds later when it was all over, my tank had been knocked out and my crew and I had miraculously escaped.

Fear is a subjective sensation associated with the production of adrenalin and so on. Moments such as those described above are usually so fleeting that they are over before the physiological reaction of the human body has time to operate. Whilst riding a motor cycle at night I once hit a hole in the road and got into a bad skid. It was obvious that I was going to crash but, again, I did not have time to feel afraid. Nor, when wounded during the war, did I feel pain until later, when I was back in safety. Many friends have told me the same: pain only comes afterwards when one has time to think.

In general, lions do not take human victims unless for reasons of age or other disability they are unable to capture their normal food. But there are some striking exceptions and, once a lion has become a man-eater, its cubs may acquire the habit also. The typical man-eater becomes very cunning and wary, rarely returning to his kill and moving about the country, which makes him difficult to hunt. Professor Frank Debenham (1955) relates the following story which occurred in the Kasungu district of Malawe. 'A lion had got into a hut in which a boy was sleeping, probably by falling through the thatched roof and could not find its way out again. The yells of the boy brought father and mother from the next hut and when they had pushed down the doorway they saw the lion with its forepaws on the boy and its stern towards them. The man caught hold of its tail to pull it off his son but the lion dug its claws into the ground and the boy and held on. The man then bit the lion's tail but that too had no effect so he got his head farther into the hut and bit the lion's rump, still pulling the tail. Then the woman crawled into the hut to try and pull the boy out, but with a lightning sweep of one paw the lion felled her and held her down and he did the same thing with a man who also attempted a rescue. The father had to keep up the pull on the tail or all would have been killed, but finally a lamp and an axe were brought. There were then others to help in the tail-pulling and the father reached under the lion and cut the foot that was holding down his wife. Finally he reached over the back of the lion and killed him by hitting him on the head. All the wounded recovered and are alive today and who can say, in the light of that story, that the African is not brave and resourceful?—the resource in this case being to keep up the pull on the lion's tail so that its feet were occupied in keeping itself in position over its captives'.

Lionesses with cubs are dangerous animals to approach and, in such circumstances, often charge upon slight provocation. Occasionally they will abandon their offspring without attempting to defend them. According to L. J. Tarlton lions, and especially solitary males are more apt to attack. Sir Alfred Pease wrote that no rule can be laid down as to when a lion will, or will not, charge. A very hungry or vicious lion or one that has previously been hunted, shot at or wounded may attack unprovoked but, in general, a lion does not charge unless he has been persistently followed on foot, ridden after, shot at or wounded. Major J. Stevenson-Hamilton records an instance in which some game rangers, while following lion tracks, once walked right into the middle of five while they were lying sound asleep in some long grass. The animals sprang up and rushed away. So close were they that one of them knocked a man down with its hind-quarters, but they made no attempt to injure anyone, their energies appearing to be concentrated upon escape.

Although most big game animals are usually timid and shy and their 'charges' often simply the result of blind haste, it is clear that lions in particular should always be treated with respect.

Leopard

When at bay, the leopard is a most courageous and dangerous animal. Unlike a lion, he may be relied upon always to charge home. Although man-eating leopards are occasionally recorded, they are rare, possibly because Africans are better able to deal with them than with lions and never permit an animal to survive after an offence of this nature. An extreme instance is cited by Debenham (1953) of a leopard in the Kasungu district of Malawe which had killed 37 people before it paid the penalty.

F. Le Vaillant (1790), however, mentioned that when gazelle hunting near the Cape, he came face to face with an enormous and furious 'panther'. He expected every minute to be devoured but the animal was driven off by his dog! At Torit, Equatoria, I met a man who had lost an eye when he drove off a leopard that was attacking his cow. The Sudanese say that it is possible for a strong man to strangle a leopard provided that he hunches his shoulders so that his neck is not broken by a blow from the animal's paws.

Of leopards, Sir Samuel Baker (1890) wrote that: 'In every country the natives are unanimous in declaring that the leopard is more dangerous than the lion or tiger, and I quite agree in their theory that when any dangerous animal is met with, the traveller should endeavour to avoid its direct gaze. It is an error to suppose that the steady look from the human eye will affect an animal by a superior power, and thereby exert a subduing influence; on the contrary, I believe that the mere fact of this concentration of a fixed stare upon the responding eyes of a savage animal will increase its rage and incite attack. . . . A leopard will frequently attack if it is certain that your eyes have met, and it is always advisable, if you are unarmed, to pretend to disregard it, at the same time that you keep an acute look-out lest it should approach you from behind. Wherever I have been in Africa, the natives have declared that they had no fear of a lion, provided that they were not hunting, as it would certainly not attack them unprovoked; but that a leopard was never to be trusted, especially should it feel that it was discovered'. I do not doubt that Baker was correct.

Hyaena and hunting-dog

Troops of hunting-dogs often show great indifference to man and a reluctance to retire before him. This fearlessness is sometimes attributed to natural ferocity but, as far as humans are concerned these animals are not dangerous. Large hyaenas, on the other hand, have occasionally been known to kill people at night. W. M. Kerr (1886), for example, mentions seeing Africans who had been mauled by a 'wolf', including one woman who had lost an eye.

An amusing incident is described by Dr. Anders Sparrman (1785) in the following words: 'At a feast near the Cape one night, a trumpeter who had got his fill was carried out of doors, in order that he might cool himself, and get sober again. The scent of him soon drew thither a tiger-wolf, which threw him on his back, and dragged him along with him as a corpse, and consequently a fair prize, up towards *Table-mountain*. During this, however, our drunken musician waked, enough in his senses to know the danger of his situation, and to sound the alarm with his trumpet, which he carried fastened to his side. The wild beast, as may easily be supposed, was not less frightened in his turn. Any other besides a trumpeter would, in such circumstances, have undoubtedly been no better than wolf's meat'.

When Alan Moorehead (1959) was camping by Kilimanjaro he tucked a pair of leather shoes under his bed because he had been told that the hyaenas in those parts had a special predilection for good solid tanned boot-leather. He thought that his shoes would be safe, however, because 'wild animals loathe and fear the human smell, and although they may approach quite close out of sheer curiosity they will not come into the camp itself. Often in the morning you will see the tracks of some large animal, a rhinoceros perhaps, not fifty yards from your tent. The tracks, a series of large rosettes in the dust, come on very steadily until suddenly the animal has picked up the hateful scent in the air, and you can see where he has wheeled sharply away into the bush.

'It seemed therefore incomprehensible to me on this night that I should have been woken by a strange presence in the tent. It was not so much a presence as a smell; a smell so vile, so absolutely sickening, it appeared for an instant to be an imaginary thing, part of a particularly bad dream perhaps. I groped for a flashlight and something an inch or two away from my face vanished into the darkness. All this was a great joke in the morning when the boys searched everywhere and found not so much as a trace of a hobnail from my shoes. Even the rubber heels had been eaten. After that I slept with my second pair of shoes inside my bed.

'Hyenas have amazing savagery and determination. One alone will drive away a cheetah, the great spotted cat which is the fastest thing alive. (When some years ago cheetahs were raced against grey-hounds in England the cheetahs jumped clean over the greyhounds' backs to get to the front.) Two hyenas will force a leopard to abandon a kill; a dozen of them will defeat a lion'.

Moorehead clearly appreciates, what so many writers do not, that the hyaena is an attractive and interesting animal quite different from the cowardly thief that he is usually supposed to be. The miserable, mangy-looking specimens so often exhibited in zoological gardens bear little resemblance to the alert, furry creatures of the wild.

Buffalo

Opinions vary as to how dangerous buffalo are. F. C. Selous (1893), who had immense experience of them, declared that he did not consider them naturally vicious for he wrote: 'Though the buffalo of Central South Africa when wounded will usually charge its pursuer if it sees him close at hand, yet, if he is at a distance of over fifty yards, it will only do so in exceptional cases. Although many accidents happen in the pursuit of these animals, yet, in my opinion, the danger incurred in hunting them is marvellously exaggerated. Having shot altogether nearly 200 buffaloes to my own rifle, and followed very many of them when wounded into very thick bush, I think I have had sufficient experience to express an opinion on the subject. I know of several instances where buffaloes have charged suddenly, and apparently in unprovoked ferocity, upon people who never even saw them until they were dashed, in many cases mortally wounded, to the ground; but I believe that, in at any rate the majority of cases, if the whole truth could be made known, these buffaloes would be found to have been previously wounded by some other hunter, and finding themselves suddenly confronted by another sportsman in the thicket or patch of long grass to which they had retired to brood over their injuries, at once rushed upon the intruder, perhaps more from the instinct of self-defence than anything else'.

A buffalo always charges with its horns laid back in the sides of the neck and the nose straight out in a line with the back. Conse-quently it is very difficult to hit the brain and a bullet through the chest, right through the heart, even with a heavy rifle, will not stop a charge at close quarters though it will of course kill within a short time.

Considering their build, buffaloes are extremely swift and even in the open a horse will have to gallop hard to avoid being overtaken. On one occasion, F. C. Selous had a horse killed under him by a buffalo which then turned upon him as he lay on the ground. He threw himself to one side and just avoided the upward thrust of the horns receiving, however, a severe blow on the shoulder. Luckily the animal then turned and galloped away.

When wounded and followed up, a buffalo is, of course, a dangerous animal, tough and plucky. It will hunt a fugitive as a terrier hunts a rat. Animals suffering from old wounds are equally dangerous but, unless molested, only old bulls are naturally aggressive to man.

Following a wounded buffalo in thick bush. From F. C. Selous (1881).

Walter Bell (1960), the great elephant hunter, wrote of the buffalo as follows: 'Why buffalo should have earned such an evil name for dreadful cunning and great ferocity has always rather puzzled me. In the hundreds that I have encountered during my hunting career I have never been charged, and yet I have constantly read of fierce encounters between hunters and this game. Once, when I came suddenly on a buffalo bull lying wounded in thick stuff he did not charge. This animal had been mauled by a lion and according to all rules he should have charged as soon as he became aware of my approach. . . .

'Among the cases of maulings that have come under my own personal observation, or that I have heard at first hand from my friends, the maulings by buffalo have been far more frequent than the deaths. The wounds caused by buffalo horns seem to heal better than those caused by lions. The dirty teeth and claws of old lions almost always cause dangerous infection if antiseptics are not applied very promptly'.

In his journal for May 1888, T. H. Parke gave a description of the kind of injury a buffalo can cause. 'In the middle of my high fever yesterday [4 May 1888], I was obliged to walk a distance of over three miles in the heat of the noonday sun, to see one of our men, Mabruki Wadi Kassan, who had been nearly gored to death by a wounded buffalo. The infuriated animal had caught him with one of its horns between the thighs, tossed him into the air, and then trampled on him as he lay on the ground after falling. I found the perinaeum so completely laid open, that the bladder and adjacent portions of the intestine were fully exposed. He also had several ribs broken, and his head was severely bruised. His companion had escaped similar treatment by nimbly climbing up a tree, while the buffalo's attention was concentrated on the victim whom he had secured'.

It has sometimes been claimed that herds of buffalo will charge together. Captain H. C. Brocklehurst (1931) wrote, however, that he had been up to scores of buffalo, both singly and in herds, but had never known unwounded animals to make any attempt to attack. 'As one walked up towards them, they would snort and stamp and probably walk a few paces towards one with their heads up and looking very fierce, but, on making any sudden movement, they would whisk round and gallop away in a cloud of dust. . . . Buffalo, as well as other animals, when shot at, will often run towards the shot, especially when they do not know from which direction it has come. I remember shooting a buffalo in a herd, which was lying down in the open. The whole herd sprang to their feet and galloped towards me. I ran to meet them, waving my hat, and the herd divided and passed on each side.

'Sir Alfred Sharpe, writing to *The Field*, "This happened to me on one occasion, and seeing I might be trampled I stood up and waved my arms, when the herd divided to right and left and passed well clear of me" '.

G. Schweinfurth (1873) was once roused by a heavy dull sound that seemed to shake the ground like an approaching earthquake. His camp was extensive but, large as their numbers were, the whole camp was thrown into commotion, and shouts and gun-shots were heard from every quarter. The explanation of the uproar was that an enormous herd of buffaloes in their nightly wanderings had come scampering down upon the position, and exposed them, he thought, to the manifest risk of being trampled to death. Needless to say nobody was even injured.

Many big-game hunters have, at some time or other, dispersed a

charging herd of buffalo by waving their hat or stick to split the
herd in two. Clearly buffalo can be considered dangerous only when
wounded or conscious of attack.

Baboons

Baboons are normally fairly shy but when in numbers are sometimes aggressive. Thus Mansfield Parkyns wrote in 1853 that he had
heard of them in Ethiopia attacking women whom they may have
occasionally met in the roads or woods. On one occasion he was told
of a woman who was so grievously maltreated by them that, although
she was succoured by the opportune arrival of some passers-by, she
died a few days after, from the fright and ill-treatment she had
received. There are a few other accounts of baboons attacking human
beings, but, in general, they cannot be regarded as dangerous
animals.

Reptiles

Misconceptions about snakes abound, and crocodiles are often
mistakenly regarded as being extremely dangerous. Very few snakes
are naturally aggressive, however. Cases of pythons attacking human
beings must be most exceptional. David and Charles Livingstone
(1865) merely commented that they are harmless and said to be good
eating. Although there are a few records of mambas attacking a man
without apparent warning, this also is an unusual occurrence.
Poisonous snakes may, however, strike in self-protection or when
trodden on, but so-called 'charges' are probably merely efforts to
escape to some hiding place.

Crocodiles are really scavengers like jackals, vultures and
marabou storks. They readily assemble, especially at night, to feed
on a carcass, and have frequently been observed in the water dis-
membering buffaloes, zebra, water-buck or the carcasses of other
crocodiles discarded by skinners. Despite their unenviable reputation, Dr. Hugh B. Cott[11] has shown that only large specimens regularly feed on mammalian food and human fatalities are comparatively
rare. Dinka fishermen treat them with scant respect and will wade
in the water to spear fishes, merely pushing crocodiles out of the
way.

John Petherick (1861), however, described an unprovoked attack
by a crocodile on an Egyptian fellah who was working a *shadouf*
on the Nile, south of Khartoum. The reptile suddenly darted at him
from out of the river, allowing him barely time to jump into the
excavation in the embankment formed for the working of his lever.
'Singing out lustily for help, he was followed by the open-jawed

[11]1961, *Trans. Zool. Soc. Lond.* **29**, 211-356.

reptile, the onslaught of which was so furious that it jammed its shoulders so effectually between the sides of the pit—partially open towards the river-side—that, notwithstanding all its efforts, it could neither advance to seize its prey nor retire. The position of the man, as he forced himself to the utmost limits of his small prison, roaring for assistance, and invoking the Prophet and saints, may be imagined; whilst the fearfully-armed mouth of his enemy, threatening instant death, was extended within a span of his chest. His cries were unheard; but his comrades, attracted at length by the interruption of the water, came to his assistance, and, spearing with a lance the helpless reptile, the fellah was released'.

Mr. and Mrs. Petherick (1869) also recounted a curious tale of a crocodile that lived on an island called Geizet-il Arab in Upper Egypt. 'Going the round of the island, three crocodiles escaped into the river, and on closely investigating the spot, a quantity of eggs were discovered in the sand. No sooner had they made off with their booty in the direction of a small tent which they had pitched than a crocodile, having watched their proceedings, rushed to the place of her deposit, and as rapidly returned to the river, and, swimming, followed them opposite to their destination, where until nightfall her eyes were perceptible above the water. Their repast that night was a rich one; but as soon as the last embers of their fire had died away, the crocodile charged them furiously, repeating her attack several times during the night, and it was only by the frequent discharge of their firearms that they kept her from closing upon them. From that time the crocodile, hitherto harmless, became furious, and fell upon all the cattle it could catch upon the river-side. Among many victims was a fine mare belonging to an Arab in the village of Nega' t-il-Arab, half an hour's walk from the river. The mare, as is usual, was allowed her freedom to graze in the coarse abundant pasturage, and, whilst drinking, was suddenly seized in the back of the neck by the jaws of the crocodile. The mare being an animal of great power, in an agony of pain, violently threw up her head, and with it the crocodile, which dropped on her back, and, with her unwonted burden, she galloped off to her stable. The astonished villagers belaboured the crocodile so heartily with their *naboot* (stout sticks, common to every Fellah) that it was soon induced to let go its hold and dismount; but the mare died from the joint effects of its wounds and the fright'.

Baker (1890), too, was not at all sympathetic to crocodiles, for he wrote: 'I have lost so many men by these creatures that I made a point of shooting every crocodile that showed its head above the surface, or that was basking upon the shore. . . . On one occasion I killed a crocodile which, although not longer than 12 feet 3 inches, was very thick in the body; this was proved to be a malefactor by the testimony of two bracelets and a necklace, belonging to a missing girl, which we found within its stomach'.

Continuing with a list of the 'accidents' that had occurred to his expedition, he mentioned one man who had his arm bitten off at the elbow while collecting aquatic vegetables from the bank. He was saved from utter loss by his comrades, who held him while his arm was in the jaws of the crocodile. The man was brought to me in dreadful agony, and the stump was immediately amputated above the fracture. Another man was seized by the leg while assisting to push a vessel off a sandbank; he also was saved by a crowd of soldiers who were with him, engaged in the same work: this man lost his leg.

'The captain of No. 10 tug was drowned in the dock vacated by the 108 ton steamer, which had been floated into the river by a small canal cut from the basin for that purpose. This channel was about 30 yards in length, and 3 feet in depth. No person ever suspected that a crocodile would take possession of the dock, and it was considered as the safest place for the troops to bathe. . . . Finally, Sai'd of No. 10 steamer was wading across the canal by the same dock where Rais Mahomet was killed, when a tremendous crocodile rushed like a steamboat from the river, seized him by the waist, and disappeared'.

A. St H. Gibbons (1904) described an incident on the Zambesi which, he claimed, demonstrated the length to which the crocodile would go, 'in districts where he has become accustomed to the succulence of human flesh', during which his launch was charged by one. 'Then there came a sharp knock delivered in the steelwork immediately below my feet, and a large crocodile had realised—it is to be hoped with some inconvenience to himself—that he was not equal to six and a half tons dead weight. The shock, however, was sufficiently severe to give to those for-ard the impression that we had struck a rock. The brute at once dived into deep water, and perhaps it as well for me that he made the attack direct instead of resorting to "tail" tactics. Crocodiles have been known to charge canoes in this manner with a view to shaking the occupants into the water'. Elsewhere he records that at Kazungula 'a crocodile had entered a hut occupied by a sleeping native, and, seizing him in his powerful jaws, dragged him to the river, where he disappeared with his prey'.

On the other hand, David and Charles Livingstone (1865) found that the Shire river teemed with fish of many kinds and the only time when its crocodiles were dreaded was when the river was in flood. 'Then the fish are driven from their usual haunts, and no game come down to the river to drink, water being abundant in pools inland. Hunger now impels the crocodile to lie in wait for the women who come to draw water, and on the Zambesi numbers are carried off each year. The danger is not so great at other seasons'.

It is interesting to note that, as long ago as 1814, Henry Salt thought that in Ethiopia the danger of crocodiles was exaggerated by the local population. 'We occasionally observed several crocodiles called by the natives agoos, rising at a distance to the surface of the river: they appeared to be of enormous size and of a greenish colour. The natives of Abyssinia in general seem to entertain a more than usual dread of this animal; for, if anyone goes to the Tacazze even to wash his hands, he takes a companion with him to throw stones into the water for the purpose of keeping off the crocodile; and in crossing a ford, it is usual with the natives to carry their spears and to make as much noise as possible, though these animals are seldom known to frequent the shallower parts of the stream: while the very thought of bathing in the river seemed to strike them all with horror'.

The following extract from the narrative of the travels of D. Denham and H. Clapperton (1826), during which Lake Chad was first seen by Europeans, suggests that crocodiles, even when large, need by no means always be regarded as dangerous. 'The banks were thickly scattered with trees rich in foliage, and all hung over with creeping plants, bearing various coloured and aromatic blossoms, amongst which the purple convulvulous flourished in great beauty: several crocodiles, from eight to fifteen feet in length, were slumbering on the banks, which, on our near approach, rolled into the stream, and disappeared in an instant. The natives appeared to fear them but little in shallow water, but dived in with great boldness after the ducks we shot, and a large iguana that we struck while sleeping on a tamrind tree, and which fell headlong into the river'.

According to J. Bland-Sutton (1911): 'The danger which human beings run from crocodiles appears to vary in different localities. In the Nile, these reptiles are dangerous to men, and particularly to women who fetch water from the river. In many parts of the river the risk is so appreciable that it is the custom to fence off the watering places with stakes, to prevent the women being seized by crocodiles when dipping water. The fear of crocodiles is hereditary among natives throughout the whole of Africa. The frequent reports of trustworthy observers indicate that large crocodiles lie in ambush in shadowy parts of the river, or swim in the water like a log of wood, and suddenly knock an unwary man or woman into the water with a swish of their powerful tails. When fishing in crocodile-haunted water it is dangerous to stand too near the river's brink.

'Authentic reports are available of boys being dragged into the water by crocodiles when leaning over the side of a canoe. A. H. Neumann, when sitting in his tent by the shore of Lake Rudolf, was suddenly alarmed by a scream: on rushing out he was horrified to see his gun-bearer in the jaws of a large crocodile. The man had been seized whilst bathing.

'A man in the jaws of a crocodile has fewer chances of escape than one in the power of a lion, for the scene of the tragedy is in the water, and its action is very swift. The leading features of such dreadful events are: A loud and piteous scream of terror, a violent agitation of the water near the spot where the victim was standing, which only lasts for a few minutes, and the tragedy is complete'.

The above accounts clearly indicate that large crocodiles can occasionally be aggressive and dangerous to man.[12] On the other hand, it is obvious from the studies of Dr. H. B. Cott that it is really quite exceptional for human beings to be eaten and even attacks on game and domestic animals do not appear to be heavy. No doubt imagination plays a large part in the horror with which crocodiles are so often regarded.

Conclusions

Before attempting to summarise the information given in this chapter, I would like to give some expert opinions on the aggressiveness and dangerousness to man of African big game. First, an incident which befell E. S. Grogan and A. H. Sharp (1900) near Bor in the southern Sudan. 'Following the river, we made good progress till a halt was called by the presence of a stupendous old bull elephant with magnificent tusks, who was dozing on the path. We shouted to him to get out of the way, and he slowly turned round, stalked towards us, and when within fifty yards curled up his trunk, spread his ears, rumbled, and came. Crash went every load, and I found myself in a medley of tents and boxes, pots and pans, with a double .303 loaded with soft-nosed bullets, looking at him in amazement; but the shot fortunately turned him, and away he went, screaming and trumpeting, giving my blankets a parting kick as he swung round. This is the only time I have ever seen one aggressive without due cause'.

It might be considered that to be rudely awakened during a midday doze would be sufficiently disturbing to merit some display of bad temper on the part even of the most good-natured of elephants.

Grogan and Sharp also pointed out that 'lions and buffaloes, and, in a lesser degree, elephant, when fired at have a habit of moving towards the shot to investigate matters, especially if they have not

---

[12]Crocodiles sometimes attack small boats, possibly irritated by the sound of outboard motors (Richardson, J. & Livingstone, D. *Copeia* **1962**, 203-4).

previously caught the sportsman's wind. It is an unpleasant habit, and with a little imagination is easily transformed into a furious charge. Another shot, however, or a sudden movement will generally send them rushing off. I believe that this habit is the mainspring of nine-tenths of the bewildering adventures with which books of African travel are so freely loaded. . . . Elephant hunting seems to be the most dangerous when one is hunting, but lion hunting is in reality. Fewer lions than elephants by far have fallen to the rifle, yet there have been many more fatalities with the former. In the same way, buffalo hunting gives the impression of being very desperate, but the number of casualties is very small in proportion to the enormous number of buffalo that have been killed. It is the fearful rapidity of the lion's charge and the extreme improbability of stopping such a comparatively small beast in the difficult country which he usually selects for his last stand, that constitutes the great danger of his pursuit'.

Opinions differ as to which is the most dangerous game animal in Africa or, rather, which of elephant, lion, buffalo and rhinoceros. Sir Samuel Baker put the elephant first, the rhino second, the buffalo third and the lion last. However, as E. A. Temple-Perkins (1955) points out, it is apparent from Baker's books that he never aimed at the correct heart shot on the elephant and knew nothing of the frontal shot. Dashing about on a horse and shooting at elephants' shoulders, as he did, does not make for longevity—but he got away with it! Many of the older South African hunters shared Baker's views on dangerous game, presumably for the same reason.

In order to make an impersonal assessment, Temple-Perkins devised a system by which marks were awarded to each animal for those traits, including the acuteness of their senses, that contribute to their dangerousness as antagonists of man. According to this, the lion came first, followed by the elephant, buffalo and rhino. This view is in agreement with that of Frederick Courtney Selous who was perhaps the greatest hunter of all. 'When lions are met with in the daytime, they almost invariably retreat before the presence of man. . . . If pursued or wounded, however, they may be expected to charge, and . . . a far larger proportion of them do charge than of any other animal in southern Africa with which I am acquainted; and as their powers of concealing themselves, and their quickness and agility in attack, are far greater than in the elephant, buffalo or rhinoceros, I pronounce them to be more dangerous animals to meddle with than any of these'. To which Temple-Perkins added: 'The lion's quickness and agility in attack must be seen to be believed. It is easily the fastest of the four animals, with a top speed of 50 m.p.h.—roughly double that of the elephant. The buffalo is credited with 35 m.p.h. and the

Wildebeest, Ngorongoro, Tanzania

Water-buck, Uganda

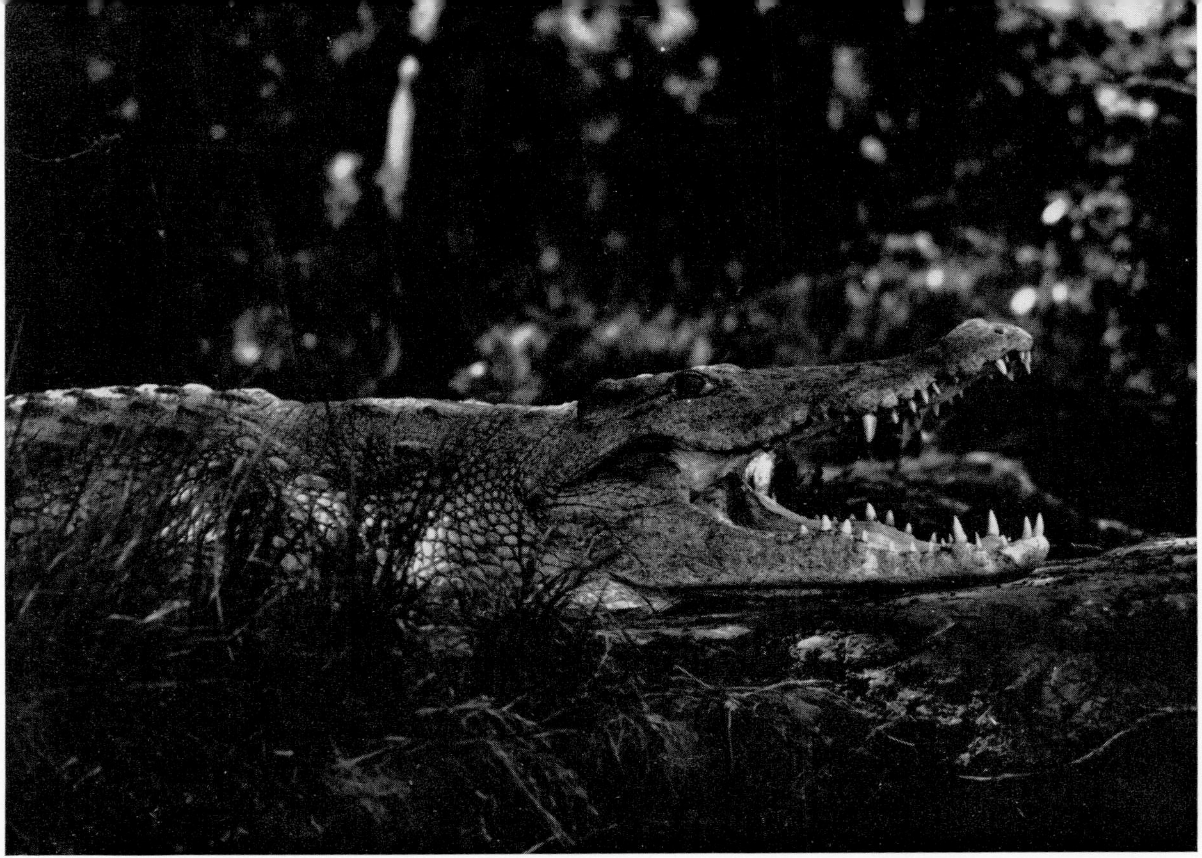

Crocodile, Paraa,
Murchison Nile,
Uganda

rhino with 28 m.p.h. These figures may be compared with the race-horse's 45 m.p.h. and the greyhound's 36 m.p.h.'.

Mansfield Parkyns (1853) who lived for thirty years in Ethiopia was convinced that, unless provoked, wild beasts never attack man. 'The only animal spoken of by the natives of this country as having the daring to do so is the rhinoceros; but as I have never had an intimate acquaintance of him, I cannot pretend to pronounce as to his character. A single male elephant will attack anything; but this can no more be taken into consideration than the acts of a dog when under the influence of hydrophobia; for the elephant, thus separated from the herd, appears to be nearly in a state of madness, wantonly destroying every object he can lay trunk upon'.

David and Charles Livingstone (1865) commented on the tameness of animals that had not been hunted with fire-arms: 'Our path leads frequently through vast expanses of apparently solitary scenery; a strange stillness pervades the air; no sound is heard from bird or beast or living thing; no village is near; the air is still, and earth and sky have sunk into a deep, sultry repose, and like a lonely ship on the desert sea is the long winding line of weary travellers on the hot, glaring plain. We discover that we are not alone in the wilderness; other living things are round about us, with curious eyes on our movements. As we enter a piece of wood-land, an unexpected herd of pallahs, or waterbucks, suddenly appears, standing as quiet and still, as if constituting a part of the landscape; or, we pass a clump of thick thorns, and see through the bushes the dim phantom-like forms of buffaloes, their heads lowered, gazing at us with fierce untameable eyes'.

Describing the East African scene at the end of the last century, Capt. Sir John C. Willoughby (1889) wrote: 'The grassy plain through which we marched was simply crawling with hundreds of Granti, wildebeeste, hartebeest, and zebra, the last two being singu-larly tame, watching us with idle curiosity, and never attempting to move before we got within fifty yards of them; then with a buck and a bound they started off, stopping every forty or fifty yards to turn and take another good look at us'.

According to David and Charles Livingstone (1865), 'The scent of man is excessively terrible to game of all kinds, much more so, probably than the sight of him. . . . Is this the fear and the dread of man, which the Almighty said to Noah was to be upon every beast of the field? A lion may, while lying in wait for his prey, leap on a human being as he would on any other animal, save a rhinoceros or an elephant, that happened to pass; or a lioness, when she has cubs, might attack a man, who, passing "up the wind of her", had unconsciously, by his scent, alarmed her for the safety of her whelps;

or buffaloes, and other animals, might rush at a line of travellers, in apprehension of being surrounded by them; but neither beast nor snake will, as a general rule, turn on man except when wounded, or by mistake. If gorillas,[13] unwounded, advance to do battle with him, and beat their breasts in defiance, they are an exception to all beasts known to us. From the way an elephant runs at the first glance of man, it is inferred that this huge brute, though really king of beasts, would run even from a child'.

The accounts of old hunters, like Sir Percy Fitzpatrick, of the timidity and shyness of antelopes and other wild animals, provide a clear indictment of the disgraceful way in which the fauna of Africa was persecuted until a few decades ago. The more that game animals are observed at first hand, the more it becomes impressed on the watcher how little aggressive ferocity is to be found amongst them. Even carnivores seeking their prey at night will usually avoid man unless driven by extreme hunger. Wounds, fear, surprise or the need to defend the young may temporarily change the peaceful tendencies of a wild beast, but the concept of nature 'red in tooth and claw' seems to be largely a figment of the imagination.

[13]The gentle, shy nature of the gorilla was not known until comparatively recently. J. L. C-T.

The last charge. From S. W. Baker (1866).

CHAPTER VII

PACHYDERMS

THE relationship between Europeans and the game of eastern Africa dates from earliest recorded history. In this and the two following chapters I shall give brief accounts of this relationship with respect to the species that have attracted most attention, viz., elephant, rhinoceros, hippopotamus, lions, leopards, hyaenas, hunting-dogs, antelopes, buffalo, zebra, pythons and crocodiles. At the same time, I have added a few points of general interest about the relationships between these animals and man.

Elephants

When the people of Tarentum (a Greek town in Southern Italy) had provoked the Romans to war about 280 B.C., they bargained with Pyrrhus, king of Epirus, to come to their assistance. Pyrrhus brought an army of 22,000 infantry, 3,000 horses and 20 elephants —strange beasts never before seen in Europe—with armed men in castles on their backs, and a battle was fought at Heraclea in the province of Lucania. The simple Roman soldiers called the elephants 'Lucanian cows'[1] and 'snake-hands', and were discomforted no less than were the horses of their cavalry. For not only was this the first occasion that Roman troops (two legions under command of Valerius Laevinus) met with the solid Macedonian phalanx, but the elephants were not used in the orthodox fashion as weapons of assault. Pyrrhus stationed them in the wings of his army to frighten the Roman cavalry with their smell and monstrous trumpeting, for untrained horses will not face them. Hannibal, who was an admirer of Pyrrhus, employed the same tactics at the battle of Trebia (218 B.C.) with the elephants he had brought over the Alps.

After the first setback, with typical courage and efficiency, the Roman soldiers thought of a way of dealing with the terrifying creatures. At the next battle they attacked with chariots in which stoves were carried and red-hot sling bullets routed the opposing elephants, which became more of a menace than an asset as they

---

[1] *Boves Lucae*, a poetic term used by Lucretius with reference to the Carthaginian elephants of the Punic wars. Some authorities suggest that it was also a term of derision used by the soldiers.

spread disorder in the king's ranks. The elephants of Pyrrhus were probably the only Asiatic ones (*Elephas indicus*) to figure in the wars of Italy, because those used by the Carthaginians were almost all, if not entirely, African.

The Romans themselves seldom used elephants in warfare except for their moral effect against barbaric tribes. For example, a small number was sufficient to terrify the Gallic tribe of the Allobroges so that they were crushingly defeated on the Rhône in 121 B.C. by Domitius Ahenobarbus, one of the ancestors of Nero. Julius Caesar during his short campaign in Egypt, which he described in the famous despatch 'Veni, Vidi, Vici', wrote to Rome for 40 elephants, remarking that they would of course be of no use except to make a show. Although it is frequently stated that Claudius used an elephant corps in the invasion of Britain (A.D. 43), there is no evidence for this. The story may have originated in an attempt to explain remains of extinct elephants dug up in Sussex in the sixteenth and seventeenth centuries.

Not unnaturally, the Romans very much disliked fighting against elephants and attempted by political and economic means to discourage their use by other nations who might become potential enemies. It is said that during the first of the wars between Rome and Carthage (Punic wars), the consuls who commanded in Sicily were forced to abandon the plains because their troops refused to camp except in inaccessible mountains. Nevertheless, in a battle at Palermo in 250 B.C. the Carthaginians under Hasdrubal lost 60 of their dreaded elephants which became confused in the Roman trenches and turned on their own men. During the second Punic war a method of attacking from the side with javelins was devised, and there are several accounts of individual acts of the very greatest bravery.

Probably the first occasion on which Europeans encountered elephants in warfare was during Alexander's Persian campaign. At the battle of Gaugamela in 331 B.C., Darius had 15 Asiatic elephants from Archasia, but his horses were not trained to them so he could not use them in line with his main forces to prevent Alexander's cavalry from charging. In consequence, despite their large number of scythed chariots, the Persian forces were routed and the elephants captured. These were the ones so carefully described by Aristotle. Pliny, who was a less reliable observer, said that serpents were the chief enemies of elephants and suffocated them by placing their heads in their trunks !

During his Indian campaign, Alexander had several elephants of his own which the enemy had abandoned on the banks of the Indus, and Taxiles gave him over 50. At the battle of the Jhelum (326 B.C.)

the Indian king Porus had 200 elephants like walking ramparts in the centre of his army, with archers in the wings. Although Alexander inveigled the Indian cavalry into charging and routed them, his Macedonians still had the elephants to deal with. They made a frontal attack. There was a terrific struggle in which many elephants were killed and wounded, and the Indian army was defeated. Porus too was wounded, and rode slowly away on his beautiful elephant which Alexander afterwards named Ajax. When taken prisoner he was asked how he expected to be treated. He answered: 'Like a king', and so Alexander treated him.

The Macedonians, however, had suffered very considerable losses too, including 1,200 seriously wounded, and were badly shaken by their desperate battle with the elephants. Indeed, Seleucus, one of the generals, never forgot his experience, and later when he became a king himself ceded whole provinces in order to obtain enough war elephants, which became the symbol of his dynasty. No doubt it was the fear of another battle against large numbers of elephants which was chiefly responsible for the refusal of Alexander's soldiers to go further. From that time forth, elephants played an increasingly greater part in history, and were a decisive factor in many wars.

In the spring of 312 B.C., Ptolemy of Egypt attacked and defeated Demetrius the son of Antigonus, king of Syria, at Gaza. Although the latter was outnumbered, he had 43 elephants; but Ptolemy's soldiers carried a barrier of iron stakes and chains to hold these up while they, themselves, attacked with spears. Eleven years later at the Battle of Kings, although both armies had approximately 70,000 foot and 10,000 horse, Seleucus Antiochus and Ptolemy possessed 120 chariots and in addition the former had 480 elephants against the 75 of Antigonus. Demetrius opened battle with a dashing cavalry charge, but he went too far and Seleucus's elephants cut him off. Antigonus was defeated and died with the pathetic cry 'Demetrius will save me!'

A very interesting battle took place at Raphia, south of Gaza, nearly a century later in 217 B.C., between Seleucus Antiochus III of Syria and Ptolemy IV of Egypt. Antiochus had the larger army: 62,000 infantry, 6,000 horse and 102 Indian elephants, while the Egyptian force was composed of 50,000 foot (not 70,000 as Polybius says), 5,000 horse and 73 African elephants. At first Ptolemy's right wing advanced, but on the left his elephants gave way. Few ventured to close with the Indian elephants: they were terrified of the smell, trumpeting and greater size of the latter, for quite apart from the men in the castles, the elephants themselves engaged in battle with tusks interlocked, forehead to forehead straining with indescribable fury often until one or other was killed.

Ptolemy, however, extricated himself from his flying cavalry, rode to the centre of the infantry who were better disciplined than those of the enemy and succeeded in defeating Antiochus' central phalanx. After this débâcle the quest for African elephants seems to have declined. L. Scipio, in the battle of Magnesia (189 B.C.) against the same Antiochus, recognized that his African elephants were inferior to the Indian beasts and kept them in reserve. This was the Romans' first great fight in Asia.

There has recently been much controversy over the statements of Polybius and other early authors, that the African elephants were inferior in size and strength to the Asiatic species, for it is usually assumed today that the contrary is the case. There are, however, two main sub-species of African elephant: the larger Bush elephant (*Loxodonta africana africana*), and the smaller Forest elephant (*L. africana cyclotis*). Ptolemy's animals were trapped in Abyssinia, Somaliland and the eastern Sudan, by expeditions based on the Red Sea coast near Suakin and shipped to Egypt in a fleet of 'elephantoforoi'. Modern critics assume that the sub-species was *L. africana africana*, and that the ancient historians were ignorant or untruthful. T. R. Glover[2] thought that there might once have been a smaller variety, and Jennison (1937) suggests that the chief reason for the inferiority of the African elephants was that too few were captured to allow effective selection of suitable animals, and many of those used were immature. In India, great numbers were captured for all types of work and only the strongest tuskers were used in war. Even so, one Indian army had no less than 9,000 elephants, while the biggest drive by the Carthaginians under Hasdrubal in 205 B.C. produced only 140. Further, the natives of Ethiopia killed great numbers by hamstringing and shooting them with bows worked by three men, and no bribe from Ptolemy III could persuade them to forgo this sport.

Secondly, the treatment and training of newly captured elephants was not properly understood, and lastly their large ears obstructed the mahout. It might be added that the temperament of the two species is not the same, and the comparative weakness of the trunk of the African species may have had an effect, for the animals were taught to fight with their trunks as well as their tusks. We read of Roman soldiers being killed and hurled considerable distances. Elephants were also taught to execute criminals and prisoners of war.

On the other hand, Sir William Gowers[3] gives a number of reasons for believing that the African elephants trained for war by the Ptolemies and the Carthaginians may well have belonged to the

[2](1935) *The Ancient World*. Cambridge: Univ. Press.
[3](1948) *African affairs* **47**, 173-80.

Forest species, which would account for their inferiority. The range of *Loxodonta africana cyclotis* is wide even today, and extends from the Atlantic coast south of the Sahara to the Nile valley. Two thousand years ago it must have been far more extensive. Elephants lived among the forests on the foothills of the Atlas Mountains, and Hanno saw them on the shores of the Atlantic about 500 B.C. No doubt this forest belt was connected in pre-historic times with the forests of Senegal and Sierra Leone where the Forest elephant is still the predominant species.

The recorded weight of 34 tusks presented to the temple of Apollo at Didyma by Ptolemy XI, the father of Cleopatra, gives an average of under 40 lb. a tusk. Although these were probably the finest procurable, yet they are small in comparison with selected tusks of *L. africana africana* which may weigh 100 lb. or more (p. 146). The small size of the elephants on Carthaginian coins is suggestive, as well as the fact that in none of the accounts of the battles of the Punic wars is there word of a howdah or turret carrying an armed crew, although mahouts (*rectores* or *Indi*) were mentioned. Perhaps the Carthaginians found that their elephants were not strong enough to carry such a weight without detriment to mobility. Nor did they have to meet hostile elephants in battle.

Finally, the Forest elephant has been successfully trained on a large scale in modern times, but attempts to train the Bush species have met with little success. The few which have been kept until maturity in zoological gardens have all become unmanageable and dangerous, and Gowers considers it unlikely that this species could have been trained for war.

A valuable safeguard against elephants panic-stricken in battle was invented by Hasdrubal. The mahout carried a sharp chisel (scalprum) and mallet, so that he could break the animal's neck and kill it instantly in an emergency.

Elephants were considered the Royal beasts of the Roman emperors, but sometimes they were given as a reward for exceptional valour. For example, Cornificius, who saved a cohort in Sicily, was allowed by special permission to ride one in the streets of Rome. Elephants were frequently exhibited at the Roman Games, but were seldom killed. More often they gave displays of dancing and performed tricks. Both Julius and Augustus Caesar maintained herds near Ardea and Laurentum, and they may have bred there, but the Imperial government made no use of them in war.

The interest of the elephant as a spectacle dates from earliest times. During the 9th century B.C., Assurnasirpal II established a zoological garden containing a number of elephants caught in Syria and others lived in a zoo at Kalhu in Phoenicia. Ptolemy II (283-246 B.C.) sent expeditions down the Red Sea to Aqiq (18°N) for the capture of elephants and founded a settlement known as Ptolemais Therm. Bernice, half-way to Suez, developed as a port of disembarkation because navigation was difficult in the Gulf of Suez. The elephants, like the Carthaginian war elephants, when not on active service, were probably kept in public parks where the populace could see them.

The first elephants to be seen in Rome were the four Indian elephants captured from Pyrrhus when, on his second invasion of Italy, he was defeated near Beneventum by a Roman army under M. 'Curius Dentatus (275 B.C.). Twenty-four years later, L. Metellus brought over 100 African elephants which he had taken from the Carthaginians in his great victory at Panormus (Palermo) in 251 B.C. The captured animals were ferried across the Sicilian straits on a raft built of barrels and were exhibited in all the towns that lay on the route to Rome, according to Jennison (1937).

According to Pliny, the earliest use of elephants in the bloody ritual of the Roman amphitheatre was during the consulship of M. Antoninus and A. Postumius. The poor beasts were at first set to fight each other but, in later shows, were opposed by armed men. Under Julius Caesar they were sometimes matched against horse and foot soldiers—20 elephants versus 500 men. As an elaboration, each elephant was provided with a tower and 60 defenders and 20 of these units were set against 500 horse and 500 foot soldiers. Under Claudius and Nero, the final item in the circus was always a contest between a single gladiator and an elephant. At a later date, and to a much greater extent, elephants were trained to do various tricks but it is not clear whether these were the Indian or African species.

An early account, in English, of the African elephant is given by Murray (1817) in which it is stated that: 'Only one species of this genus is peculiar to Africa, and is named the African elephant. Its head is roundish, forehead convex, ears large, and the surfaces of the grinders have lozenge-shaped ridges. It appears to have only three toes or hoofs on the hind feet. It inhabits Africa from Senegal to the Cape of Good Hope. It is not known if it extends along the east coast of Africa, or if it is there replaced by the Asiatic species. At present the African elephant is never domesticated; although it appears from historians that the Carthaginians trained them for war and for various domestic purposes'. Prof. F. E. Zeuner (1963) comments that, as a beast of burden and for lumbering, elephants were not greatly valued in the ancient world where human slaves were in good supply. They are not efficient workers except in jungle where man and other domestic animals do not succeed.

Even today, there is no certain evidence of the domestication of African elephants before Ptolemaic times. It seems highly probable, however, that they must from a much earlier period have been captured and tamed for military purposes at least in the Nile valley, says Carrington (1958). Pliny has described how the animals were driven by horsemen into narrow defiles where they were enclosed until rendered tame by the effects of hunger. But, whereas Asian elephants have long been regarded as useful servants of mankind, the African species has only been trained on a large scale since 1899 when Commandant Laplume founded an elephant-catching station in the Belgian Congo. That elephants are extremely intelligent animals has long been known but, in the case of the African species, this quality was seldom made use of except by the Carthaginians. Elephants have been known to use branches as fly-whisks, which indicates a surprising degree of insight for a wild mammal, and several authors have described incidents in which members of a herd have assisted young or wounded animals.

An extraordinary display of animal loyalty was witnessed by W. H. Winter[4] whilst on elephant control duties on Mount Elgon in western Kenya. Three elephants, members of a herd comprising about 30 bulls, cows and immature animals were shot in a large forest clearing. A fresh breeze was blowing from the direction of the herd, on account of which the confused and furious beasts could not tell whence the danger lay. They milled around trumpeting and shrieking fearfully, throwing up showers of grass and stones in their fury. Then, with incredible determination and complete disregard for their own safety, they attempted to lift their dead companions. Bewildered and enraged as they were, they pushed and butted ponderously at the inert forms, entwining their trunks with those of the dead animals in their efforts to lift them. For more than half an hour they persisted in their attempts to move their stricken comrades and showed no other interest or fear.

Presently a large cow advanced to where one of the elephants lay and knelt beside it, placing her tusks under its belly. She then tried to stand, her body tensed with the tremendous effort. Suddenly there was a loud crack and her right tusk snapped off above the root, describing an arc through the air and landing about 30 feet away. Shortly afterwards, the herd moved off, making a terrific commotion. But three times they returned, stampeding through the forest, trumpeting and screaming incessantly, to renew their efforts at moving the dead animals. It appeared as though they were trying desperately to communicate with them, in order to get them to their feet and move off to safety: their anguish at the inability of their companions to rise was obvious.

[4](1964) E. Afr. Wildl. J. 2, 163-4.

Records of elephants coming to the assistance of their wounded comrades are commonplace in the annals of hunting and the account given above is by no means unique. Everyone who has had experience, both of African and Indian elephants, seems to be in agreement that they are unusually intelligent members of the animal kingdom.

During the last few decades people have begun to interest themselves in African elephants for scientific and aesthetic reasons. Until the present century, however, they were used only for war, ceremony and circus, or as a source of meat and ivory. As A. Sparrman wrote in 1785, 'It is merely for the sake of the teeth that the elephants are hunted by the colonists, though at the same time they contrive to preserve the flesh for their servants, viz. their slaves and Hottentots. As the larger elephant teeth weigh from one hundred to one hundred and fifty Dutch pounds, which may be disposed of to the government for as many guilders, so that a man may sometimes earn three hundred guilders at one shot, it is no wonder that the hunters of elephants are often so extremely venturesome'.

It is unfortunately true that, since Roman times, man's interest in African elephants has been very largely centred on their tusks. However, unless one was extremely lucky, even in the old days, it was usually necessary to walk many miles and spend many days in travel to get even one elephant with good tusks.

John Hanning Speke wrote in his diary for 3 December 1863: 'We pushed forward as best we could to a pond at the western end of the district, where we found a party of Makua sportsmen who had just killed an elephant. They had lived in Ugogo [Tanganyika] for one year and a half, and had killed in all seventeen elephants; half the tusks of which, as well as some portion of the flesh, they gave to Magomba for the privilege of residing there'.

In his journal for 1 February 1877, as recorded in his book, *Through the Dark Continent* (1878), H. M. Stanley wrote: 'While mustering my people for re-embarkation, one of the men came forward and said that in the principal village there was a "Meskiti", a "Pembé" a church, or temple, of ivory—and that ivory was "as abundant as fuel". In a few moments I stood before the ivory temple, which was merely a large circular roof supported by thirty-three tusks of ivory, erected over an idol 4 feet high, painted with cam wood dye, a bright vermilion, with black eyes and beard and hair.... One hundred other pieces of ivory were collected, in the shape of long wedges, long ivory war-horns, ivory pestles to pound cassava into meal, and herbs for spinach, ivory armlets and balls, and ivory mallets to beat the fig-bark into cloth'.

Many thousands of bull elephants were killed in South Africa during the second half of the last century but, of these, although a few of abnormal size have been recorded, probably less than 50 carried tusks weighing more than 100 lb. each. One obtained from the Lake Ngami district in 1873 weighed 174 lb. but it is not known whether it came from a single-tusked elephant or not. Another killed between the Vungo and Gwelo rivers, within 70 miles of Bulawayo in 1868 or 1869 had tusks measuring over 9 ft. in length and together weighing over 300 lb. A pair of tusks of the same weight was obtained from Umzila, king of the Gaza Zulus in 1874. The elephant with the largest tusks shot by a European in South Africa was killed on the Zouga river in 1849. Although quite a small bull, the aggregate weight of its tusks was between 230 lb. and 240 lb. and their length rather less than 8 feet.

In East Africa, male elephants accompanying the herds of cows commonly have tusks of about 50 lb. each, while the average of those of other bulls would be from 60 to 80 lb. V. L. Cameron (1877), however, met in Tanganyika a caravan of elephant tusks some of which were so immense that they required two men to carry them. Some idea of their weight may be formed when it is remembered that a Mnyamwesi porter will bear up to 120 lbs. of ivory as a load.

Sir Samuel Baker (1890) mentioned that he saw in Khartoum a pair of tusks that weighed 300 lbs. and he saw a single tusk of 172 lbs. In 1874 a tusk was sold at the ivory sale in London that weighed 188 lbs. Baker added, 'These specimens are exceptions to the general rule, as the average weight in a full-grown African male would be about 140 lbs. the pair, or 75 lbs. for one tusk and 65 lbs. for the fellow, which is specially employed for digging'.

According to Lydekker (1926) the world's record for a single tusk is $226\frac{1}{2}$ lbs. This came from an elephant shot with a muzzle-loader on Kilimanjaro at the beginning of the century by a slave, who belonged to a notorious slave and ivory hunter named Shundi. This tusk was exported from Zanzibar and is now in the British Museum (Natural History). It measures 10 ft. $2\frac{1}{2}$ ins. in length with a girth of $24\frac{1}{4}$ ins. Its fellow is reported to have been of similar dimensions. An elephant carrying the largest tusks ever shot by a European was killed by Major P. H. G. Powell-Cotton in the Lado Enclave in 1905. These tusks scaled 198 and 174 lbs., the larger being 9 ft. long and 25 ins. in circumference.[5]

In the American Museum of Natural History there is a pair of East African tusks, of which one measures 11 ft. $5\frac{1}{2}$ ins., and the other 11 ft. in length, but their united weight is only 293 lbs. Of a pair of tusks from the White Nile in 1905, one weighed $159\frac{1}{2}$ lbs. and measured 7 ft. 11 ins. in length, while the weight of the other was $135\frac{1}{2}$ lbs. and its length 8 ft. 3 ins.

[5]Brocklehurst, 1931.

W. D. M. Bell shot in all 1,011 elephants during his career. From his best safari (Bell, 1923) he brought back 14,780 lbs. of ivory. He estimated that the average march on foot for each elephant, including distances to and from the hunting areas, was about 73 miles and that he wore out 24 pairs of boots in a year. Of his total, 983 were large bull elephants with big tusks.

An animal as dramatic as the elephant naturally gathers to itself innumerable folk tales and myths, of which only a couple of examples are given because they fall within the realm of anthropology rather than of history or zoology. Elephants have also appeared in art since Upper Palaeolithic times.

The Wangwana and Wanyambu informed H. M. Stanley (1878) with the utmost gravity that the elephant maltreats the rhinoceros frequently, 'because of a jealousy that the former entertains for his fiery cousin. It is said that if the elephant observes the excrement of the rhinoceros unscattered, he waxes furious, and proceeds instantly in search of the criminal, when woe befall him if he is sulky, and disposed to battle for the proud privilege of leaving his droppings as they fall! The elephant in that case breaks off a heavy branch of a tree, or uproots a stout sapling like a boat's mast, and belabours the unfortunate beast until he is glad to save himself by hurried flight. For this reason, the natives say the rhinoceros always turns round and thoroughly scatters what he has dropped'.

According to Unyoro traditions, in ancient times a man had an honest son, but he himself was violent, and had taken many cattle from his neighbours. Once upon a time he ordered his son to go and occupy a neighbour's house; if he did not do so he threatened to kill him. The son went and slept in that house, but found in the early morning that the inhabitants had fled. He durst not return home, whilst by himself he would have starved; so he prayed to the 'great Magician' to rescue him, and was thereupon, together with the house, turned into an elephant.[6]

Numerous other elephant legends persist in modern African folklore and the subject has been discussed at some length by Richard Carrington (1958) and Albert Jeannin (1947). A complicated magical ritual, as already mentioned (p. 21), until very recently preceded native elephant hunts. Its object was not only to assure a successful outcome to the hunt but also to propitiate the spirit of the dead animal so that it would not avenge itself on the hunters.

Rhinoceroses and Hippopotamuses

'There are two animals, named frequently in scripture, without naturalists being agreed what they are. The one is the behemoth,

[6]Emin Pasha, 1888.

the other the reem, both mentioned as the types of strength, courage,
and independence on man, and as such exempted from the ordinary
lot of beasts, to be subdued by him, or under his dominion'. So wrote
James Bruce in 1790 of the elephant and rhinoceros. He continued:

'Isaiah,[7] who of all the prophets seem to have known Egypt and
Ethiopia the best, when prophecying about the destruction of
Idumea, says that the reem shall come down with the fat cattle; a
proof that he knew his habitation was in the neighbourhood. In
the same manner as when foretelling the desolation of Egypt, he
mentions as one manner of effecting it, the bringing down the fly[8]
from Ethiopia to meet the cattle in the desert, and among the bushes,
and destroy them there, where that insect did not ordinarily come
but on command,[9] and where the cattle fled every year to save
themselves from that insect'.

Isaiah was probably referring to blood-sucking horse-flies or
stable flies which have been known to kill animals by their bites
(p. 87), for it is unlikely that he could have known of tsetse flies
and 'nagana'. The distribution of tsetse is restricted by climate and
vegetation, and I doubt if conditions were sufficiently different in
Isaiah's time to have permitted them to enter Egypt.

The first record of the rhinoceros being exihibited in the Roman
arena comes from Dio, and refers to the show of 29 B.C. after the
annexation of Egypt. This rhino, and a hippopotamus which was
also killed, probably came from the zoological garden of the
royal palace at Alexandria. African rhinoceroses appeared only
occasionally in Rome: the Indian species was far more often seen.
Jennison (1937) suggests that this is because the latter is more
hardy and its expectation of life in captivity is much greater. However, Ethiopian rhinoceroses appeared during the reigns of Antoninus
Pius, and of Commodus (A.D. 180-92), son of Marcus Aurelius.

Bruce wrote of the rhinoceros in Ethiopia: 'The hunters of these
large beasts are called Agageer, from Agaro, to kill, by cutting the
horns or tendon of Achilles with a sword. I have already described
the manner of this hunting' (p. 26). 'Chardin[10] says that the
Abyssinians tame and train the rhinoceros to labour. This is an
absolute fable; besides that, we have reason to believe the animal
is not capable of instruction, neither history nor tradition ever gave
the smallest reason to make us believe this, nor is there any motive
for attempting the experiment, more than for believing it was ever
accomplished. . . . It is a general observation made in every part

[7]Isaiah, chap. XXXIV, ver. 7.
[8]Isaiah, chap. VII, ver. 18 and 19.
[9]Exod., chap. VIII, ver. 22.
[10]Chardin, tom.iii, p. 45.

where [the rhinoceros] resides, that he is indocile, and wants talents; his fierceness may be conquered, and we see, with a moderate degree of attention, he is brought to be quiet enough; but it is one thing to tame or conquer his fierceness, and another to make him capable in instruction. . . .'

Burton (1860) wrote that in his days the 'gargatan' or 'small black rhinoceros with a double horn' was as common as the elephant in the interior of Africa. 'Large horns are imported through Bombay to China and Central Asia, where it is said that people convert them into drinking-cups, which sweat if poison be administered in them: thus they act like the Venetian glass of our ancestors, and are as highly prized as that eccentric fruit the coco de mer. The Arabs of Muskat and Yemen cut them into sword-hilts, dagger-shafts, tool-handles, and small boxes for tobacco, and other articles. They greatly prize . . . the spoils of the kobaobo, or long-horned white rhinoceros, which, however, appears no longer to exist in the latitudes westward of Zanzibar island'.

The curious observation of a concert by a group of rhinos is described by Lt.-Col. J. H. Patterson (1909), who heard something that sounded like a score of elephants trumpeting together: 'We stalked on carefully and cautiously among the rocks with the wind in our favour, until at last we were able to look over the edge of a crag down into the ravine at our feet. Then the weirdest sight that I could ever wish to see suddenly unfolded itself beneath my astonished gaze. No fewer than sixteen rhinos were gathered together close by, all roaring at each other and struggling and fighting in their efforts to get at the waterhole. The moon was shedding a brilliant lustre all round, and everything was peaceful except at this one spot where pandemonium reigned'.

Apparently, apart from the attention they have attracted as objects of the chase, rhinoceroses, white and black, have not been the source of much interest. If it were not for the supposed aphrodisiac properties of their horns, it is doubtful if either species would be on the danger list.

The hippopotamus has attracted even less attention than the rhino. As I have mentioned, one was killed in the Roman amphitheatre in 29 B.C. but, even earlier, one had appeared as a curiosity in the show of M. Scaurus (58 B.C.). Hippos probably came from Egypt[11] with native keepers: they were seen in the arena at the time of Commodus, who killed six, and some were kept in captivity by Elagabalus (A.D. 218-22). The hippo, however, has long been a valuable item of food in many parts of Africa and is now being exploited commercially in Uganda.

[11]Hippos were to be found in the Nile delta until the end of 17th Century A.D.

Encounter with a lion. From D. Livingstone (1857).

CHAPTER VIII

CARNIVORES

FROM earliest times, the lion has been worshipped as a god or venerated as a sacred creature by many African, European and Asian people. He became the companion of not a few emperors and kings, has been trained to fight in battle and to pursue and kill game for his masters. The history of the lion in antiquity has been studied in detail by Gustave Loisel (1912) to whose work both Jennison (1937) and Pease (1913) pay tribute.

Lion

The ancient Egyptians worshipped lions at Leontopolis, and at Heliopolis where the sacred lion lived in the Temple of Ammon Ra. His food was most carefully selected and sacred melodies were played to him during his meals. The Egyptians not only tamed, but trained for the chase, lions, cheetahs, leopards, wild cats, hyaenas and wild dogs. In Egypt, as in Assyria, these lions were usually shaved. Lions were also used in war—Rameses II (1298-1232 B.C.) was accompanied in battle by his lion Anta-m-nekht, who went in front of his chariot alongside the horses, and struck down with a blow of his paw, anyone who came near. Under the Ptolemies, lions were still used in religious festivals and in processions. After the Roman conquest, sacred menageries continued until about A.D. 384, when the Emperor Theodosius abolished the worship of animals and destroyed their temples.

The hunting and killing of lions in Roman amphitheatres was initiated by Marcus Fulvius Nobiliar, about 185 B.C., to celebrate a successful campaign in Greece. Later, the custom of using lions for the public execution of criminals became commonplace. According to Pliny, Q. Scaevola, son of Publies was the first to exhibit a combat of many lions together. L. Scylla provided 100 lions with 'manes and collars of haire' to be hunted to death in the arena, Pompeius the Great 600 (325 of them with manes) and Caesar Dictator, 400. Probably many of these were from Syria and Iraq. Such butcheries became more frequent under later emperors. Augustus kept 260 lions in his menagerie, Germanicus 200 and Nero 300. Titus (A.D. 79-81) gave *venationes* in which 9,000 animals were killed—no doubt many

of them lions and leopards. The Emperor Hadrian is said frequently
to have paraded as many as 100 lions for the circus and in A.D. 118,
on his birthday, 100 lions and 100 lionesses. Antonius Pius and
Marcus Aurelius are each said to have shown 100 lions at one time
and Probus to have caused 100 maned lions and an equal number of
lionesses to be slain in the amphitheatre. Commodus is said to have
killed, with different weapons, 100 lions let loose at once in the arena
without needing to give any of them a second shot or blow.[1] According to F. W. Fitzsimons (1919) there are records of over 50,000 lions
captured and brought to Rome within a period of 40 years.

Pliny wrote that if a lion 'chaunce to be wounded hee hath a
marveilous eye to marke the partie that did it, and be the hunters
never so many in number, upon him he runneth onely'. However,
George Jennison, who used to be Director of the Manchester Zoological Gardens, points out that, even though particularly ferocious
beasts were chosen as man-eaters, they had to be carefully trained
for this purpose. Then, not only were they deprived of food and
water for some days before a performance, but the condemned
prisoners were instructed, by moving their hands, to irritate the
beasts and thus incite them to attack.

The charming story of Androcles and the lion relates to an incident
that probably happened at the time of Claudius. According to Aulus
Gellius, the slave Androcles, who had been condemned to the beasts,
was recognized and greeted affectionately in the arena by a lion from
whose foot when wandering as a fugitive in the desert he had
previously removed a thorn. Jennison suggests that it may have been
under Claudius that Seneca saw a lion protect from other lions a
beast-fighter who had been its keeper.

There can be no doubt that the Roman *venationes* must greatly
have reduced the population of lions in North Africa. According to
Strabo, even by the time of Augustus (31 B.C.-A.D. 14), there were
so few lions in Libya that the nomads could turn to agriculture and
were able to keep the beasts of prey under control.[2] It seems extremely
unlikely, however, that reduction in the numbers of lions should
actually have been responsible for nomads settling into agriculturalists.

Little is known of the status of lions after the fall of Rome up to
the time when North Africa was opened up by Europeans; but
doubtless the Moors and other invaders from the north would have
continued the war against the great carnivores. The Rev. Dr. Thomas
Shaw, Professor of Greek in the University of Oxford, describing his

[1]Jennison, 1937.
[2]Matheson, C. (1947). *J. Soc. Preserv. Fauna Empire* (N.S.) Pt. 55, 24-37.

travels in Tunisia, wrote in 1738 that 'whatever may be the cause, it is certain, there would be great difficulty at present to procure a fiftieth part of those lions and panthers which Africa contributed formerly to the diversions of Rome'.

In 1878, 28 lions were killed in Algeria; the following year 22; in 1880, 16; in 1881, 6; in 1882, 4 and in 1883 the last three were slaughtered.[3] Lions were recorded as still surviving in Tunisia in 1881 and in Morocco until 1920. Today, however, they are extinct north of the tropic of Cancer. At the southern extremity of the continent of Africa, lions were recorded as being not uncommon close to Cape Town in the early years of the 18th Century, as we have seen. They survived in Cape Province for more than a hundred years' later and the last recorded was one killed in 1842. The last record for Natal was in 1863 and, in the Johannesburg area, the final date is given as 1898. At the present day the lion is believed to be quite extinct in Cape Province, Natal and the Orange Free State and practically so in the western Transvaal although stragglers from the northern and eastern parts of that province occasionally occur there.[4]

Lions have always been a terror to herdsmen. A representation of two lions killing an ox was emblazoned on the noble shield made by Vulcan, at the request of Thetis, for Achilles,

> 'Two lions rushing from the wood appear'd,
> And seized a bull, the master of the herd'.

'A man who kills a lion', stated an edict of Honorius and Theodosius II of A.D. 414, 'need not fear indictment, as our subjects' safety must prevail over our pleasure; but our pleasure still forbids the hunting and selling of lions, though not their killing'.

Topsell, in his quaint *History of Four-footed Beasts* (1658) wrote of the lion : 'On the sight of man [he] is seldom found without rage. In his anger he beateth the earth with his tail, afterwards his own sides, and lastly leapeth upon his prey or adversary . . . the reason is thus rendered by Aphrodisius. The backbone of such beasts is hollow, and containeth in it marrow, which reacheth to the tail, and thereafter there is in the tail a kinde of animal motion and power . . . but we have shown before that the lion striketh his sides with his tail, for the stirring up of himself against perils. . . .'. It is true that the lion's back is comparatively weak and animals have been paralysed by a heavy blow on the spine. Also they lash their tails in anger.

According to A. Sparrman (1785) the Hottentots of South Africa 'looked upon it as a certain fact, and I have since heard the same from others, that a lion does not immediately kill the person he has got under him, unless he is excited to do so by the resistance he meets

[3]Pease, 1913.
[4]C. Matheson, *loc. cit.*

with. At length, however, it is reported, the royal tyrant gives the
coup de grace on the victim's breast with a hideous roar'. He added
that the Hottentots 'conceived the old and commonly-recurred
notion to be absolutely true, that both lions and tygers would attack
a slave or a Hottentot, before they would a colonist or a white man'.
The Hottentots reckoned fires and fire brands to be 'a great preservation and defence against lions and other beasts; they could, however,
mention instances in which the lion had leaped forward to the fire,
and carried off some of them, who had been sitting round it and
warming themselves'.

Sir John Barrow (1801) agreed with Sparrman. 'It seems to be a
fact well established', he wrote, 'that the lion prefers the flesh of a
Hottentot to that of any other creature. He has frequently been
singled out from a party of Dutch. . . . The horse, next to the Hottentot, seems to be his favourite food; but on the sheep, perhaps on
account of his woolly covering, which he is too indolent to uncase,
he seldom deigns to fix his paw'. Maybe lions had learned that
Hottentots were less able than Boers to defend themselves.

On the other hand, in his chapter 'Of Four-footed Beasts' Job
Ludolphus (*History of Ethiopia*, 1684) wrote: 'The lyon, tho' he
excel in fierceness and cruelty all the rest of the wild beasts, yet he
shews a certain kind of magnanimous respect of man. For he never
injures, unless he be ready to famish so that he do not betray his
own fear'. Moreover, Ludolphus refers the reader to Solinus who
'allows them many marks of clemency: they sooner assail men than
women; they never kill infants, unless pinched with hunger'.[5]

The Arabs of the Sudan, according to G. A. Hoskins (1835), told
some singularly superstitious tales of the generosity of the lion. 'They
say, that when the lion seizes the cow of a peasant, he will permit
the owner to carry away a portion; particularly if he asks for it in
the name of his mother, wife, or family, *and takes it without showing
any fear*'.

Other lion stories are even more fanciful, such as that which
irritated M. Parkyns (1853). 'In Abyssinia, for instance, they tell how,
among the Gallas, there are certain tribes, among whom the boys go
out to slay the lion single-handed, and armed only with a small knife
and a piece of stick a foot long: the stick being used literally *to stop
the lion's jaw*. The boy provokes the kingly animal by insulting
epithets, till he springs open mouthed at him, when, with great
dexterity, the youthful hunter thrusts his pointed stick perpendicu-
larly between the lion's jaws, after which the boy proceeds deliberately
to cut his throat with his knife. Fancy a boy holding a lion with one
hand and cutting his throat with the other! Coeur de Lion could

[5]Pease, 1913.

not have done it. I have often asked how it happened that the sportsman forgot bags for his claws—weapons far more dangerous, and more often used by all the feline tribe, than their teeth. Strange to say, old hunters have told me this story and believed it. . . .'.

Surprisingly discerning for those days, was Sir John Barrow who wrote in 1801 : 'The lion frequently measures his strength with the buffalo, and always gains the advantage. This, however, he is said to accomplish by stratagem, being afraid to attack him on the open plain. He lies waiting in ambush till a convenient opportunity offers for springing upon the buffalo, and fixing his fangs in his throat; then striking his paw into the animal's face, he twists round the head and pins him to the ground by the horns, holding him in that situation till he expires from loss of blood'. And again, 'The lion, in fact, is one of the most indolent of all the beasts of prey, and never gives himself the trouble of a pursuit unless hard pressed with hunger'.

W. J. Burchell (1824), like Sir Winston Churchill, also had no great opinion of lions, 'but of his majestic air and movement . . . while at liberty in his native plains, I can bear testimony. . . . At the time when men first adopted the lion as the emblem of courage, it would seem that they regarded great size and strength as indicating it; but they were greatly mistaken in the character they have given to this indolent skulking animal. . . .'.

The method of hunting lion on horseback used by the colonists of the Cape in the 18th century, is described by Sparrman as follows : 'It is said, that horses in battle, or in other dangerous enterprises, suffer themselves more willingly to be caparisoned by their riders than at other times; a circumstance which I think I have likewise remarked in these animals, on expeditions, where the danger, indeed, was not so great, as in hunting the buffalo and rhinoceros, when they have passed rivers, and gone up and down steep places and precipices with the greatest alacrity. Our horses, the very same as had several times, in the manner above-mentioned, shewn their disquietude when the lion happened to be in the vicinity of them, and which were not in the least trained to the chase, once exhibited a spirit in the pursuit of two large lions, equal to that which they had shewn at other times in chasing the timid gazelles. . . . It is only on the plains, that the hunters venture to go out on horseback after the lion. If it keeps in some coppice, or wood, or on a rising ground, they endeavour to teaze it with dogs till it comes out; they liquewise prefer going together two or more in number, in order to be able to assist and rescue each other, in case the first shot should not take place.

'When the lion sees the hunters at a great distance, it is universally allowed, that he takes to his heels as fast as ever he can, in order to get out of their sight; but if they chance to discover him at a small distance from them, he is then said to walk off in a surly manner, but without putting himself in the least hurry, as though he were above showing any fear, when he finds himself discovered or hunted. He is therefore reported likewise, when he finds himself pursued with vigour, to be soon provoked to resistance, or at least he disdains any longer to fly. Consequently he slackens his pace, and at length only sidles slowly off step by step, all the while eyeing his pursuers askaunt: and finally makes a full stop, and turning round upon them, and at the same time giving himself a shake, roars with a short and sharp tone, in order to shew his indignation, being ready to seize on them and tear them in pieces. This is now precisely the time for the hunters to be upon the spot, or else to get as soon as possible within a certain distance of him, yet so as at the same time to keep at a proper distance from each other; and he that is nearest, or is most advantageously posted; and has the best mark of that part of the lion's body which contains his heart and lungs, must be the first to jump off his horse, and, securing the bridle by putting it round his arm, discharge his piece; then in an instant recovering his seat, must ride obliquely athwart his companions; and, in fine, giving his horse the reins, must trust entirely to the speed and fear of this latter, to convey him out of the reach of the fury of the wild beast, in case he has only wounded him, or has absolutely missed him. In either of these cases, a fair opportunity presents itself for some of the other hunters to jump off their horses directly, as they may then take their aim and discharge their pieces with greater coolness and certainty'. No instance has ever been known of any misfortune happening to the hunters in chasing the lion on horseback.

In parts of Ethiopia, even today, to have killed a lion is considered a feat equal to having slain several men in battle and a man cannot honourably marry unless he has achieved either one or the other. In this respect, de Cosson (1877) wrote: 'It is an old custom for the warriors to assemble on a certain day before their chief for the *drum-fater*, or boast, when they unblushingly boast of all the great deeds they have done, and the men and beasts they have killed. So eager are the Abyssinians to appear at this ceremony red-handed, that occasionally they have even been known to kill some unfortunate slave in secret, in order that they might be able to boast of having slain a man'.

The food of lions varies very much from district to district. In some parts of eastern Africa, zebra appears to be their favourite prey but large numbers of antelope and sometimes giraffe are killed. It has been recorded that on one occasion a lion and lioness fought over the body of an antelope. The final result was that the lioness was killed and a considerable portion of her flesh eaten by her mate.

In places where buffalo abound, lions feed largely upon them and the art of tackling this most formidable prey is handed down from old to young by imitation. Even so, lions are by no means always successful. Game wardens recently reported a case in which a lion and lioness attacked a buffalo and all three were fatally wounded; on another occasion three lions were unable to overcome a buffalo. The skeleton of a lion and of a male gemsbok have been found together, the horns of the latter wedged through the ribs of the lion. This, no doubt, sprang and was spitted by the gemsbok which, in turn, was killed by the lion as its neck bones were crushed and broken.

According to Pease (1913), lions prefer fresh meat, but will feed on elephant and rhino carcasses, whether fresh or 'high'. Lions do not by any means always return to their kills when other prey is available, nor do they always drink water after meals. Indeed, in arid regions such as parts of Somalia and the Sudan, they may have to go for many days without water, surviving on blood and moisture from the intestines of the animals they kill. David Livingstone mentions that the lion frequently feeds on the water-melons which cover the desert lands of Africa after rain. In the Kalahari these, no doubt, provide a source of moisture.

The lion's method of killing its prey is as follows: Small animals are knocked over with a quick blow of the paw, and finished off with a bite in the neck or throat. Animals the size of a wildebeest or a zebra are usually thrown down by the impact of the lion hurling himself against the front part of the body. With one paw the attacker often catches hold of the forehead or the nose of the victim, pulling the head down to the chest so that in falling forward the animal breaks its neck. The breaking of the neck does not always take place, however, and, indeed, may well be the exception and not the rule.[6]

The lion usually focuses his attack on the front part of the body. Exceptions occur when more than one lion attacks a large animal such as a buffalo or giraffe. Then, whilst one or more lions attack from the front, another will grab the hind legs of the prey from the rear. Gemsbok have dangerously sharp, pointed horns and have been known on occasion to kill their attacker. In the Kalahari, however, where these antelopes are the staple prey of lions, kills are invariably made by leaping on the victim and breaking its back.[7]

The strength of a full-grown lion in his prime, is prodigious. He can fell an ox with a blow of his paw, crush up the bones of its neck in a moment and drag off the whole carcass to his lair. By exerting his strength, a lion can drag animals the size of a buffalo for 50 yards over flat ground but, of course, he cannot lift it much above the

[6]Guggisberg, 1961.
[7]Eloff, F. C. (1964). *Koedoe* No. 7, 105-112.

ground. Sparrman also commented that 'the lion's strength is considerable. This animal was once seen at the Cape to take a heifer in his mouth and, though the legs of the latter dragged on the ground, yet seemed to carry her off with the same ease as a cat does a rat. It likewise leaped over a broad dike with her, with the least difficulty'. Nevertheless, 12-16 farm dogs will easily get the better of a large lion. 'When these have got pretty near the lion, the latter, from a greatness of soul, does not offer to fly any farther, but sits himself down. The hounds then surround him, and, rushing on him all at once, are thus, with their united strength, able to tear in pieces, almost in an instant, the strongest of all wild beasts. It is said, that he has seldom time to give more than two or three slight strokes with his paws, (each of which strokes is instant death) to an equal number of his assailants'.

'It has been denied that lions can kill animals as large as the rhinoceros or hippopotamus; but that they can do so we found on the Thika-thika. Three lions had surprised a hippopotamus in some long grass about thirty yards from the river; there had been a desperate fight, in which the grass had been trampled down for yards around, but the hippopotamus had finally succumbed to loss of blood; its skin was terribly scratched by claws and teeth, and the lower part of the neck had been torn away'.[8]

A few years ago, two lions tried to kill a baby hippo near the mouth of the Rufiji river in Tanganyika, but the mother hippopotamus attacked them and killed one. Three days later, an adult hippo, in mad flight, burst through the piles supporting a hut, overturned it completely with its occupants inside and was then killed further on by a pursuing lion. Whether or not there was any connection between the two incidents is not clear, but it may have been that the surviving lion had again attacked a hippopotamus.

In the early days of South Africa, according to F. W. Fitzsimmons (1919), the lions had a luxurious and easy-going life for game was then plentiful. The springbucks covered the plains in hundreds of thousands and when, on the approach of the dry season, they migrated northwards to more favourable pastures, the lions would leisurely trot along like camp followers in the rear and dine off venison whenever they felt so inclined. In those days the lion fulfilled his mission in life in controlling the numbers of herbivorous animals which would otherwise have denuded the country of its vegetation. But, on the advent of man with his firearms, the lion was no longer needed and his extinction began.

When overtaken by disease, old age, worn-out or broken fangs, the lion is no longer able to capture the alert and fleet-footed antelopes

[8]Gregory, 1896.

and is forced to alleviate his hunger with rats, mice and lizards. But this does not satisfy him for long and one day he may screw up his courage to tackle a human being. In many parts of Africa, when goats and other domestic animals mysteriously disappear, the villagers say, 'Ah, there is an old, toothless lion about. We must turn out and kill him or he will begin eating us'. Occasionally, however, perfectly healthy lions acquire a liking for the taste of human flesh.

I have already mentioned the two man-eaters of Tsavo which devoured about 30 Indian railway workers in addition to numerous African villagers of whom no official record was kept. In 16 weeks during 1924, no fewer than 161 people were killed by man-eating lions near Sanga in the Ankole District of Uganda. Through the efforts of E. A. Temple-Perkins (1955), 17 lions were shot, trapped or poisoned: one of these was responsible for 84 deaths, another for over 40. Thereafter the menace ceased.

H. Melladew, in his *Sport and Travel Papers* (1909) gives the following account of an incident which occurred at Dembela on the Sudan-Ethiopian frontier. 'We had been asleep probably about two hours when a horrible shriek suddenly aroused us from our slumbers, and made us wide awake in a moment. There were cries of "Lion! lion!" and everything was commotion in the darkness, for sleep had overcome the minstrel watchman and the fires were all but out. . . . Seized by the feet when asleep round the fire, he had been dragged about four yards down to the river bed and there dropped by the lion, frightened probably by the man's own shrieks and the shouts of the others, and thanks to the plucky and determined manner in which his neighbour had held on to the brute's chosen morsel. All was confusion: the men had seized their spears and shields and were rushing about here and there, though not leaving the safe vicinity of the fire, rekindled now into an enormous blaze. One man in his excitement set fire to the dead leaves of a dome-palm, which burning up quickly into a column of flame threatened a general conflagration. The unfortunate man who had been so rudely awakened from his sleep had both his feet badly injured by the lion's teeth, the greater part of the sole of each having been torn away, but leaving the bones, luckily, intact'. This appears to be an account of the incident described by James (1883) and related on p. 120.

H. Wolhunter, Ranger, Transvaal Government Game Reserves, describes an unpleasant experience that befell him at twilight on 26 August 1904. As he was riding along he was unexpectedly attacked by a lion: 'I had no time to lift my rifle, but simply snatched my horse round to the near side, and drove the spurs in; he gave a bound which, no doubt, caused the lion partially to miss his spring, as his claws slipped on the horse's quarters, and though several ugly

wounds were inflicted he lost hold. The concussion and the subsequent violent spring of the horse caused me to lose my seat, and
simultaneously I saw a second lion rushing up from the opposite
direction. I absolutely fell into his jaws, and believe that he had me
before I ever touched the ground. I imagine these lions were after
the horse in the first instance, there being no known man-eaters in
the district. . . . The next thing I recollect was being dragged along
the path on my back, my right arm and shoulder in the lion's mouth,
my body and legs underneath his belly, while his fore-paws kept
trampling on me as he trotted along, lacerating the fronts of my
thighs considerably and tearing my trousers to shreds. . . . All the
time the lion was dragging me along he kept up a sort of growling
purr, something like a hungry cat does when she catches a bird or a
mouse, and is anticipating a welcome meal.

'My spurs kept dragging and catching in the ground till at last the
leather broke. I cannot say that my feelings at this time were at all
in accord with those of Dr. Livingstone, who in his book, if I am not
mistaken, expresses his feelings as those of dreamy repose, with no
sense of pain; I, on the other hand, suffered extremely in that respect,
while I hope I may never have again to undergo such agony of mind
as I then experienced; it seemed hard to die like that, and yet I could
see no part of a chance, not the slightest loophole of escape'.[9]

Then Wolhunter remembered his sheath knife. Fortunately he had
not lost it in his fall. After dragging him for nearly 200 yards the
lion stopped under a large tree. As it did so, 'I felt for where I judged
his heart to be, and struck him behind the shoulder—one, two—with
the energy of despair, using of course, my left hand. He dropped me
at the first stab, but still stood above me growling, and I then struck
him a third time in the throat with all the force of which I was
capable, severing some large vein or artery, as the blood deluged me'.

At this, the lion sprang away: Wolhunter yelled at him and
eventually he turned away into the darkness. His growls turned to
moans as he died but, before this, Wolhunter was able to climb the
tree in time to escape attack by the second lion which returned from
an unsuccessful chase after the horse.

Fortunately lions are not usually so aggressive and M. Parkyns
(1853) gives an amusing account of the consternation caused in
Eritrea by a perfectly inoffensive animal. 'Two worthy merchants
were returning in the evening to Moncullon, after having finished
the affairs of the day at Massawa, and, only one of them being
possessed of a mule, he accompanied his friend with a seat on the
crupper. They were ambling along at a comfortable pace, no doubt
discussing the past day's market, when, on suddenly turning a corner,

[9]Pease, 1913.

formed by some bushes growing near the roadside, they beheld, to their great dismay, an enormous lion seated in the middle of the road, and quietly looking at them. As Balaam's ass of old saved his master's life by standing still, so did the mule in question, by running away, at a pace which, considering the double load he carried, would have been astonishing under any other circumstances. The lion, however, apparently paid little or no attention to their movements....'.

In various parts of Africa, ancient and modern, the lion has been an object of respect, worship or superstition. Even today, in parts of East Africa, among certain tribes when a lion is killed the carcass is brought before the chief who does homage to it by prostrating himself on the ground and rubbing his face on the muzzle of the beast.[10]

In several African tribes the king, or chief, on his death, is supposed to take up residence in a lion. For this reason, in many places, lions are regarded as sacred or can only be hunted on the direct orders of the ruler of the tribe. Not only does this superstition increase the terror of the villager when he meets the lion, but it prevents him from reporting its depredations. As Professor Frank Debenham (1955) comments: 'After all, it would be a little unfair to one's great-grandfather to go and tell the police that he was responsible for the last murder down the road'.

David Livingstone (1857) whilst travelling along the southern bank of the Zambesi towards its mouth found himself in a district where there were 'a great many lions and hyaenas, and there is no check upon the increase of the former, for the people, believing that the souls of their chiefs enter into them, never attempt to kill them; they even believe that a chief may metamorphose himself into a lion, kill anyone he chooses and then return to the human form; therefore when they see one they commence clapping their hands, which is the usual mode of salutation here'. In consequence, he stated, these beasts were so abundant that his party often passed little huts made in trees, indicating the places were some of the inhabitants had slept when benighted in the fields. As numbers of his men frequently left the line of march to take certain birds from their nests, or to follow the honey guides, 'they excited the astonishment of our guides, who were constantly warning them of the danger they thereby incurred from lions'. This was south of the Zambesi near the rivulets Kapopo and Ve, slightly north of the Lobole Hills.

Miss Alice Werner wrote in 1906 that the Mankara, who occupy the angle between the Zambesi and its northern tributary the Shire river, also refrained from killing lions because they believed the spirits of dead chiefs to enter into them.

[10]Matheson, *loc. cit.*

More than half a century after Livingstone's journey, R. C. F. Maugham (1910) wrote: 'South of the Zambesi and near the Mozambique Company's boundary on the Mupa River, lions are particularly abundant, and many man-eaters occur. To such an extent, indeed, do they carry their depredations that it is no uncommon experience to pass large well-built villages which have been completely abandoned owing to the number of people taken. In these districts it is not unusual for the native huts to be enclosed in a high palisade designed as a protection, and interwoven with thorn bushes, but in spite of these precautions great casualties occur'. It is probable, however, that Maugham's inference was incorrect and that another explanation, such as sleeping-sickness, should have been given for the abandonment of the villages.

As Colin Matheson comments, the belief which protected the lion and permitted its unchecked increase even in an area where it was frequent and dangerous, shows the caution necessary in assessing the probable reaction of primitive man to his animal environment. This is illustrated by the following account which was related to H. M. Stanley (1890) by Emin Pasha who found a tribe exceedingly partial to lions; in fact, one of them would prefer to be killed than be guilty of the death of a lion. These people dug a pit at one time for buffaloes and such game to fall into, but it unfortunately happened that a lion was the first victim. The Sudanese who discovered it were about to kill it, when the chief vetoed the act and implored that the lion should be given to him. The Sudanese were willing enough, and curiously watched what he would do with it. The chief cut a long stout pole and laid it slant-wise to the bottom of the pit, up which the lion immediately climbed and bounded away to the jungle to enjoy his liberty.

J. G. Frazer (1894) wrote in *The Golden Bough*: 'In Latuka, a district of the Upper Nile, lions are much respected, and are only killed when they prove very troublesome or dangerous. There used to be in this region a lion-chief as he was called, who professed to have all lions under his control and who actually kept several tame lions about his house. Whenever a lion was accidentally caught in a trap near the station of the Egyptian Government, this man would regularly present himself and demand the release of the noble animal. The favour was always granted, and planks were let down into the pit to enable the imprisoned lion to climb up and escape'.

A. Sparrman (1785) claimed that the negroes in the more northern parts of Africa used to catch lions in pits, but did not dare to eat their flesh in case other lions should be revenged on them. But the Hottentots informed him that they did so and that they regarded the flesh as good and wholesome. No doubt primitive people first ate lions in order to acquire those qualities of strength and courage which they attributed to the 'king of beasts'. At the same time they may have preserved them as game which only chiefs were fit to hunt. According to J. G. Frazer, women in North Africa used to give their male children a piece of lion's heart to make them fearless and in many parts of Africa it was believed that lion's flesh would make a coward brave. The Rev. Dr. Thomas Shaw mentioned in 1738 that the flesh of the lion was held in great esteem in Tunisia, having no small affinity with veal, both in colour, taste and flavour.

David and Charles Livingstone (1865) met a man at a Kebrabasa village on the Zambesi who was believed to be able to change himself into a lion. 'Smelling the gunpowder from a gun which had been discharged, he went on one side to get out of the wind of the piece, trembling in a most artistic manner, but quite overacting his part'. They were told that he assumed the form of the lion and remained in the woods for days and was sometimes absent for a whole month. His considerate wife had built him a hut or den in which she placed food and beer for her transformed lord, whose metamorphosis did not impair his human appetite. At times he employed his acquired powers in hunting for the benefit of the village. After an absence of a day or two his wife took medicine into the forest which enabled him to change back into a man. Then he would return to the village and send the people to fetch the buffalo or antelope that he had killed when he was a lion, or rather found when he was patiently pursuing his course of deception in the forest.

It was also believed that the souls of departed chiefs entered into lions and rendered them sacred. On one occasion, when the Livingstones had shot a buffalo, a lion came close to their camp and roused everyone with his roaring. 'Tuba Mokoro, imbued with the popular belief that the beast was a chief in disguise, scolded him roundly during his brief intervals of silence. "You a chief, eh? You call yourself a chief, do you? What kind of chief are you to come sneaking about in the dark, trying to steal our buffalo meat? Are you not ashamed of yourself? A pretty chief truly; you are like the scavenger beetle, and think of yourself only".'

'Like most other African races, the Niam-Niam believe in evil spirits and that the soul after death enters into the bodies of certain wild animals. The Dinkas seem to believe that their dead spirits go only into hyaenas, and howl at night, but the Zandi take a wider view'. So wrote J. G. Millais (1924), adding: 'Whilst Captain Richards was stationed at Meridi, a few years ago, a lion came one night and killed a woman on the high road close to the village. Early next morning, as Richards had important business, he could not go out to attack the lion, but sent word to the local chief to send men at once to surround the lion, which was lying up in a thicket close to his kill. Richards intended to go out later and try and kill the lion when cornered, but to his chagrin he found nothing had been done and no attempt had been made to carry out his plans. Accordingly, next day he sent for the chief, who came most reluctantly, and Richards asked him why he had not obeyed his order. The reply was that neither he, the chief, nor any of his relatives would for a moment molest the lion, as it contained the spirit of his dead brother, and that to kill it would be nothing less than an act of murder. Various families of Zandi are supposed to pass in spirit form after death into different animals such as leopards, hyaenas, buffalo, giant eland and other antelopes, and these animals are immune from molestation by the family whose kinship is recognised'.

According to Commander V. L. Cameron (1877) a native of Ukaranga, on the shores of Lake Tanganyika 'asserted that in the village next to that in which he lived the people were on most friendly terms with the lions, which used to walk in and about the village without attempting to injure anyone. On great occasions they were treated to honey, goats, sheep, and ugali, and sometimes at these afternoon drums as many as two hundred lions assembled. Each lion was known to the people by name, and to these they responded when called. And when one died the inhabitants of the village mourned for him as for one of themselves'.

Throughout history the relations between man and lions have been confused by two conflicting factors. On the one hand there has been the urge to destroy or capture them, on the other to protect them for religious or superstitious reasons or, more recently to preserve some remnants of the magnificent wildlife so rapidly dwindling in the face of human competition.

Leopards, hyaenas and hunting-dogs

After the third century B.C., 'African beasts', a term which came to mean lions and leopards or 'leopards and other *variae*' (large, spotted or striped beasts) were seen more and more frequently in the *venationes* of the Roman arena. Owing to this imprecise terminology, it is usually not possible to know which species of carnivora was meant—leopard,[11] cheetah or hyaena. Augustus recorded that 3,500 *Africanae bestiae* were killed in his 26 *venationes* and this number must have included many leopards as well as lions. According to Jennison (1937) a single batch of animals described as *Africanae* would have consisted wholly or mainly of leopards and other spotted cats. This is supported by the fact that Pliny, in a passage dealing with animals of the leopard class mentions a decree of the Senate

[11]The name *leopardi* was used for maneless lions.

forbidding the importation of *Africanae* into Italy. Moreover, there is no mention of lions *and* African beasts at a single show though there are records of African beasts and bears. Actually, Africa, in the Roman imagination, was pre-eminently the home of terrible beasts so that the word *Africanae* was used for Asiatic lions as well, probably, as tigers.

An unprecedented display of *variae* was given by M. Scaurus as aedile in B.C. 58, when 150 of these animals were let loose together in the arena. Many of them probably came from Asia, however, since Scaurus had served in Syria for six years, first as Pompey's lieutenant and then as acting governor of the new province after its annexation Three years later, Pompey, in addition to the elephants and lions already mentioned, showed 410 *variae*, again probably of mixed origin. Pliny did not record the numbers in the animal shows of Julius Caesar but 420 were exhibited together by Augustus and 600 were killed at the dedication of the Theatre of Marcellus in B.C. 11. Titus (79-81 A.D.) gave *venationes* in which 9,000 animals were killed including, undoubtedly, many *variae*. Jennison suggests that the decree of Senate, referred to above, although ineffectual, was probably inspired both by the expense and the dangerousness of African beasts.

Whether or not the Ethiopian striped hyaenas reached Alexandria in Ptolemaic times is unknown, but the first mention of these animals in the Roman arena is in the *Historia Augusta* of Antoninus Pius (138-61 A.D.). In this, mention is made of the *corocota* which Diodorus gives as the Ethiopian name of an animal which, from his description, was evidently a hyaena. The Greeks and Romans must have known very well the common spotted hyaena (*Crocuta crocuta*) but, as Jennison says, though easy to capture and tame, the animal is cowardly and would be unsuited to a *venatio*. But, in the reigns of Antoninus Pius and Septimius Severus (193-211 A.D.), striped hyaenas (*Hyaena hyaena*) were sent as presents from Ethiopia and these were the specimens shown to the public. Certainly hunting-dogs (*Lycaon pictus*) were also consigned to the arena, but Jennison only mentions the type of trap in which they were caught.

When the men of the stone age penetrated into South Africa from the north, they attacked the leopard and, driving it forth from rock shelters and caves, took possession of them. The leopard had little to fear from these wild men but, with the advent of the pygmy Bushmen, it had a more formidable enemy to contend with, for they stalked and killed it with poisoned, bone-tipped arrows. The Bantu tribes, in their turn, were even stronger: they combined to hunt the leopard from its lair with dogs, and slew it with their spears, for they owned flocks and herds which fell an easy prey to prowling carnivores. The efforts of the Kaffirs, however, probably did not diminish the numbers of leopards much because, although they must have killed many, their stock would have provided an easier prey than the wild antelopes which the leopards previously had to feed on. But, when the European colonists came with their firearms and gun-traps, the leopard finally met his master. For, when hunted by dogs, it takes to the trees, where it is easily shot.[12]

The leopard is an adaptable animal and thrives throughout most of eastern Africa. It is courageous, cunning and, when cornered or wounded, will charge with the greatest fury and determination. Usually nocturnal in habit, nevertheless in dense forest it often hunts by day, killing bush-bucks, duiker, bush-pigs, guinea-fowl and francolins. In open rocky country, however, it usually preys on baboons. In parts of Africa, extermination of leopards has not infrequently resulted in plagues of baboons, which have then become agricultural pests.

Baboons in numbers are formidable adversaries and, in *Jock of the Bushveld*, Sir Percy Fitzpatrick (1907) gives a dramatic account of a captured animal being rescued from a leopard by the united effort of his troop. 'The long spotted body was crouched on a flat rock just below the baboons; he was broadside to us, with his fore-quarters slightly raised and his face turned towards the baboons; with wide-opened mouth he snarled savagely at the advancing line, and with right paw raised made threatening dabs in their direction. His left paw pinned down the body of a baboon. The voices from the mountain boomed louder and nearer as, clattering and scrambling down the face, came more and more baboons: there must have been hundreds of them; the semi-circle grew thicker and blacker, more and more threatening, foot by foot closer. The tiger [leopard] raised himself a little more and took swift looks from side to side across the advancing front, and then his nerve went, and with one spring he shot from the rock into the bush'.

I have already commented on the amazing strength of the lion. The leopard, too, is fantastically strong for its size. Sir Percy Fitzpatrick describes how a hunter who had shot a young giraffe, carried off as much as he could put on his horse and hid the rest. But when he returned next morning it had disappeared and the spoor of a full grown leopard told him why. He followed the drag mark up to the foot of a big tree, and found the remains of the carcass, fully 300 lb. in weight, in a fork more than 20 ft. from the ground.

When Mary Kingsley (1897) was in Gabon in September 1895, 14 goats and five slaves were killed in eight days by leopards. 'In Oijon', she wrote, 'when a leopard is killed, its body is treated with

12Fitzsimons, 1919.

great respect and brought into the killer's village. Messages are then sent to the neighbouring villages, and they send representatives to the village and the gall-bladder is most carefully removed from the leopard *coram publico*, each person whipping their hands down their arms to disavow any guilt in the affair'. This burning of the gall was not ju-ju, however, it was done merely to destroy it as it was believed to be deadly poison.

David Livingstone, in his *Last Journals* (1874), commented on the burning of a leopard which had been killed by native hunters: 23 April 1866: 'When we marched this morning we passed the spot where an animal had been burned in the fire, and on enquiry I found that it is the custom when a leopard is killed to take off the skin and consume the carcass thus, because the Mahondé do not eat it. The reason they gave for not eating flesh which is freely eaten by other tribes, is that the leopard devours men; this shows the opposite of an inclination to cannibalism'.

P. B. du Chaillu (1861) remarked that, in parts of equatorial Africa, the dried brain of a leopard, mixed with other charms, was believed to give its possessor dauntless courage and good fortune during the hunt. Leopards certainly receive more respect, both from Africans and from Europeans, than do hyaenas.

The hyaena is often described in uncomplimentary terms as an unattractive scavenger, vile and repulsive. This view is surprising: probably more game animals, especially when young, are killed by hyaenas than by any other carnivore. Even game up to the size of a zebra is pulled down. Spotted hyaenas are very fond of donkeys and have been known to kill adult human beings. Hyaenas show a degree of gregariousness but, according to Dr. L. Harrison Matthews,[13] do not usually hunt in packs of more than two or three although earlier writers described troops consisting of up to 20 individuals as being not uncommon. I expect it really depends on population size, because Dr. H. Kruuk of the Serengeti Research Institute has recently estimated that there are 420 adult hyaenas living in the Ngorongoro Crater, where pack-hunts of up to 30 animals can be seen on moonlit nights. In some parts of Africa the hyaena is certainly a scavenger, subsisting on carrion and bones. In others, such as the Kalahari, it is a true hunter, marauding in packs like hunting-dogs and seldom feeding on the remains of animals killed by other predators.

By extracting the identifiable hair of their prey from hyaena faeces, Dr. Kruuk[14] found that they fed mostly on wildebeest, fol-

[13](1939) *Proc. Zool. Soc. Lond.* **109** (A) 43-56.
[14](1966) *Nature* **209**, 1257.

lowed by zebra and then Thomson's gazelle. Of 1,052 hyaenas that were observed feeding, 82 per cent were devouring animals they had killed themselves, whereas only 11 per cent fed on animals killed by other predators. In the remainder, the cause of death was doubtful. However, during the day, 34 per cent of feeding animals were seen on other animals' kills, which possibly explains the popular belief that the hyaena is primarily a scavenger. Other predators take advantage of hyaena kills and probably the Ngorongoro lions obtain most of their food in this way. In general, the striped hyaena is more of a carrion-eater than the spotted species.

That hyaenas of both species are often considered the ultimate in ugliness no doubt results from unfavourable comparisons with domestic dogs to which, incidentally, they are but distantly related. Their allegedly hideous characters are, in fact, adaptive and, seen objectively, these animals are functionally beautiful. They can run at more than 40 miles per hour and have no difficulty in keeping up with their prey. Single animals will grab a wildebeest or zebra which, when it falls back, is set on by the pack and brought to the ground by bites directed at the anal regions: death usually occurs in about ten minutes.

The hyaena has a catholic diet as I have already indicated (p. 125). James Bruce (1790) wrote: 'One night in Maitsha, being very intent on observation, I heard something pass behind me towards the bed, but upon looking round could perceive nothing. Having finished what I was then about, I went out of my tent, resolving directly to return, which I immediately did, when I perceived large blue eyes glaring at me in the dark. I called upon my servant with a light, and there was the hyaena standing nigh the head of the bed, with two or three large bunches of candles in his mouth. . . . In a word, the hyaena was the plague of our lives, the terror of our night-walks, the destruction of our mules and asses, which above all others are his favourite food. . . . The hyaena . . . about Algiers is known to live for the most part upon large succulent, bulbous roots, especially those of the fritellaria, and such large, fleshy, vegetable substances. I have known large spaces of fields turned up to get at onions. . . . But the hyaena of Atbara seems long to have abandoned his primitive food of roots, if that was ever his, and to have gone largely and undeniably into the slaughter of living creatures, especially that of man. . . . There is another passion for which he is still more remarkable, that is, his liking to dog's flesh, or, as it is commonly expressed, his aversion to dogs. No dog, however fierce, will touch him in the field . . . : there was not a journey I made that he did not kill several of my greyhounds, and once or twice robbed me of my whole stock: he would seek and seize them in the servants' tents where they were tied, and endeavour to carry them away before the very people that were guarding them'.

A. Sparrman (1785) clearly appreciated the importance of the hyaena as a scavenger, for he wrote: 'Yet in this very greediness of the *hyaena* and its disposition to consume everything it can get at, the provident economy of nature is abundantly evinced. The flowery fields at the Cape would certainly soon become hideous and disfigured with carcasses and skeletons, the relicks of the great quantity of game of all sorts which graze and die there in succession, were not the *tiger-wolf* manifestly subservient to nature in the regulation of her police, by clearing her theatre from them; nay, I almost said the wolf alone: for lions and tigers, for example, never eat bones, and are not very fond of carcasses'.

Later writers have few good words for the hyaena. For example, M. Parkyns (1853) wrote of them: 'Luckily, they are as cowardly as they are big, strong and ugly, for, had they only the pluck of a toy-terrier there would be no living in a country so full of them. Nevertheless, they are said to attack children and weakly persons. They are supposed to be able to detect a faint and wearied wayfarer by the smell of his footsteps, and to follow him till, overcome by fatigue, he shall fall an easy prey, or till sleep shall give them an opportunity. They have even been known to attack persons asleep in their own houses. . . . The Abyssinians relate that in such cases (which are comparatively rare) the hyaena shows quite as much prudence as valour, for they assert positively that before attacking a healthy sleeper he will scratch him with his paw; if the man sleeps heavily (as is often the case in this country, to an almost wonderful degree), the beast will make one grab with his powerful jaws at his face or head, and be off; whereas, if disturbed by the scratching, the sleeper should start up, he will turn tail at once, leaving behind most disagreeable evidence of a highly nervous temperament. He is dangerous among domestic animals, and frequently attacks donkeys or mules'.

M. S. Wellby (1901), too, was very critical of the hyaena. 'Sometimes, when riding by moonlight, I have known hyaenas to keep pace with my horse, one on each side, for mile after mile—probably in the hope that the horse might eventually be let loose and become their prey. On one occasion I was crossing a dry vlei at about two o'clock in the morning, when I was surprised to see four or five of the brutes in single file following my last pack-mule, just as if they were dogs belonging to the caravan. They were so near, that my boy kept hitting at them with his stick to drive them away, but they did not leave us for quite a considerable time. I have never known them attack human beings in Abyssinia, but in Somaliland they used constantly to steal and carry off children, and would even bite the faces of sleeping adults, inflicting terrible wounds. It is quite extraordinary how bold the cowardly creatures will become when hungry'. It seems a bit unfair to condemn the hyaena for being, at the same time, both cowardly and bold! In any case, subjective impressions with an anthropomorphic bias have little biological significance.

I shall end this chapter with a quotation from Sparrman in which is given a reasonably accurate, although again somewhat subjective, account of the hunting-dog: 'These wild dogs are some of the most pernicious beasts of prey, particularly with respect to sheep and goats, that either the African colonists or Hottentot hoards are exposed to. They are reported not to be content merely with satisfying their hunger, but even to destroy and wound everything they meet with. They always herd together in companies, and wander about day and night after their prey. The noise they make in hunting is said much to resemble the yelping of our common hounds, only to be something softer. It is asserted that they even have the courage to try their strength with larger dogs, as well tame as wild; and that they were once bold enough in their turns to pursue a sportsman, who was out after them on horseback, but was unlucky enough to misfire. It has been observed that they hunt with much sagacity, acting perfectly in concert with each other: while at the same time each of them in particular does his best to overtake or meet the game, till at length it falls a prey to the pack. They are said to be always as lean as skeletons, and consequently ugly, and at the same time they have several spots bare of hair'.

CHAPTER IX

RUMINANTS AND REPTILES

One of the first rulers of the ancient world to interest himself in wild beasts was Ptolemy II (B.C. 238-246). Ptolemy was not only active in obtaining elephants from Ethiopia (p. 141) but paid generously for the capture of any unusual animal from that region, so that he made the Greeks acquainted with animals they had never seen before, among them the chimpanzee.

The Romans, however, were far less interested in herbivorous animals than they were in the fierce carnivores and large pachyderms. Nevertheless, new exotic beasts were sometimes imported from Africa for their shows and some were kept in captivity. The giraffe exhibited at Rome by Julius Caesar in B.C. 45 presumably came from the collection of animals at the royal palace in Alexandria. Others were seen from time to time during the following century, but not till the reign of Commodus is there a record of one being killed in the arena. Oryx antelopes were sometimes imported to fight bears or kill hounds, but the buffalo was seldom seen, no doubt because the *aurochs* were easier to capture and transport.

The zebra probably made its appearance during the second and third century A.D. when there was a decline, through over-exploitation, in the numbers of lions and leopards and the proportion of herbivorous animals in the arena increased. Giraffes appeared again during the reign of Antoninus Pius (138-161 A.D.). According to Dio, Plautianus, a minister to Septimius Severus (193-211 A.D.), 'despatched centurions and carried off from the islands in the Red Sea the horses of the Sun which resemble tigers'. These were evidently zebras which had probably been transported in dhows from the mainland of Africa to the small islands at the southern end of the Red Sea, before being forwarded to Persia.[1] One of them was killed in the ampitheatre during the reign of Caracalla (211-217 A.D.). After the decline of the Roman Empire, for many centuries the game animals of Africa were left to their own devices and the primitive hunting methods of the native tribes there.

[1]Jennison, 1937.

Ungulates

In the course of three hundred years of European settlement in South Africa, the larger species of game have given way to agricultural expansion and industrial growth until, today, they are virtually restricted to national parks and game reserves. Nevertheless, only the blaubok (*Hippotragus leucophaurus*), quagga (*Equus quagga quagga*), Cape lion (*Panthera leo melanochaitus*) and Burchell's zebra (*Equus burchelli burchelli*) have actually been exterminated. In East Africa, except for some forms of less than specific rank, no species has become extinct and most of them are still abundant, at least in restricted areas and reserves.

The blaubok, a big animal almost as large as the roan antelope, was at one time abundant on the Karoo but, by 1774, it had become scarce. A few still survived near Swellendam in 1796, the last survivor being shot in 1800. At one time the handsome quagga used to migrate in herds of 200-300 across the tropical plains of S. Africa. But the animals were slaughtered in great numbers by the Boers to feed their native labour and for their hides. The last quagga to be shot was killed in 1858, but an individual survived in captivity in the Amsterdam Zoo until 1883.

Buffalo

After reassuring the reader that in Africa there are no such animals as carnivorous bulls, whatever these may have been, James Bruce (1790) wrote that the buffalo 'is the most ferocious [animal] in the country where he resides; this, however, is not in the high temperate part of Abyssinia, but in the sultry Kolla, or valleys below, where, without hiding himself, as wild beasts generally do, as if conscious of superiority of strength, he lyes at his ease among large spreading shady trees near the clearest and deepest rivers, or the largest stagnant pools of the purest water. Notwithstanding this, he is in his person as dirty and slovenly as he is fierce, brutal, and indocile; he seems to maintain among his own kind the same character for manners that the wolf does among the carnivorous tribe'.

The Ethiopians certainly regarded their buffaloes with considerable respect, as is shown by the following quotation from M. Parkyns's *Life in Abyssinia* (1853): 'Be it known that the killing of a buffalo in Abyssinia counts as equal in merit to killing twenty men; and on this account almost every great man, and often even his children, can count a good many, as it only requires that they should be the first to wound the animal, however slightly, which they generally do with a gun or a light javelin thrown from a distance; and then it matters little who really kills it, the credit being always attached to him who draws first blood'.

Parkyns, himself, also had a healthy respect for the buffalo, which, he said, 'is more dangerous than the elephant, which seldom attacks a man unprovoked, unless it be a single male separated from the herd; while travellers who have had the ill luck to stumble on a herd of buffaloes have seldom escaped to tell the story. While I was at Rohabaita, two men, crossing the Mareb, came upon a herd; they were charged almost immediately; one, by good luck, got away among some bushes and ultimately escaped, and brought us news that his comrade was killed. We set off in search of the body, which we, with some difficulty, found in the jungle, bruised and broken to an almost indistinguishable mass by the horns and hoofs of the buffaloes'. I find this a little difficult to believe !

When David and Charles Livingstone were steaming up the Shire River in search of Lake Nyasa in August 1859, they found that game was plentiful and described the following incident with a buffalo: 'The Makololo having set fire to the grass where they were cutting wood, a solitary buffalo rushed out of the conflagration, and made a furious charge at an active young fellow named Manthanyane. Never did his fleet limbs serve him better than during the few seconds of his fearful flight before the maddened animal. When he reached the bank, and sprang into the river, the infuriated beast was scarcely six feet behind him'. In this case an attack was justified.

According to A. Sparrman (1785), the buffalo has a 'fierce and treacherous aspect. The disposition likewise of the animal seems to correspond with his countenance. He may in some sort be called treacherous as he is wont to hide himself among the trees, and stand there skulking till somebody happens to come very near him, when he rushes out at once into the road, and sometimes attacks them. This animal likewise deserves the appellation of fierce and cruel, as it has been remarked, that, not content with throwing down and killing the person whom he attacks, he stands over him afterwards, in order to trample upon him with his hoofs and heels, at the same time crushing him with his knees, and with his horns and teeth tearing to pieces and mangling the whole body, and stripping off the skin by licking it with his tongue. . . .'.

A less subjective appreciation of the character of the buffalo was given by Sir Harry Johnston in 1897: 'Buffaloes are very abundant over all British Central Africa, but of course are retiring from the vicinity of European settlements. They are also frequenters of the plain rather than the mountains, though they will ascend high plateaux in the dry season for the sake of green herbage. The favourite places of their resort are wide marshy districts like the

Elephant Marsh near Chiramo, where even after the most wanton and indiscriminate slaughter at the hands of Europeans they rest in large numbers—thousands it is said. Like the Indian buffalo they are fond of wallowing in mud and water, though perhaps not as aquatic in their habits as the last-named animal. They are dangerous beasts to tackle under certain conditions though less dangerous than the elephant and lion. It is seldom that they will take aggressive action against the sportsman when not wounded.

'Even when wounded it is doubtful whether they charge in the open. The danger in connection with shooting buffaloes is this, that the wounded beast retires into long grass or thickets. If the sportsman follows him up, then the buffalo puts no bounds to his rage and is also very cunning. He will charge from out of his hiding place and pursue his enemy with a great deal of intelligence, that is to say not altogether in a blind rage, and if he succeeds in catching him up will gore him and kneel on him. But I can obtain no authentic record of a buffalo when wounded in open country immediately charging his assailant'.

As related in Chapter VI, F. C. Selous (1881), with all his experience, did not regard buffaloes as particularly dangerous. 'When buffaloes have not been thinned out, they are usually found in herds of from 50 to 200 or 300 animals. Old bulls are oftend found alone, but more generally speaking in twos, threes, or fours. Along the Chobe I have seen as many as fifteen old buffalo bulls consorting together, and upon several occasions small herds of eight, nine or ten old patriarchs. These little herds of bulls are much more easy to approach than a large herd of cows, amongst which there are always a few wary animals on the lookout for danger. I have not found old buffalo bulls more dangerous than herd animals. Unless they are wounded, they retreat, at any rate in the great majority of cases, before the presence of man; and when wounded they are not more dangerous than herd animals under similar circumstances'.

Although a herd of buffalo is not particularly dangerous, solitary bulls may occasionally charge without warning if approached too close. The habit of wounded animals circling on their tracks and attacking their hunter has been described by many authors, as Sir Percy Fitzpatrick (1907) pointed out. 'A wounded buffalo in thick bush is considered to be about as nasty a customer as anyone may desire to tackle; for, its vindictive indomitable courage and extraordinary cunning are a very formidable combination, as a long list of fatalities bears witness. Its favourite device—so old hunters will tell you—is to make off down wind when hit, and after going for some distance, come back again in a semi-circle to intersect its own spoor, and there under good cover lie in wait for those who may follow-up'.

Despite persecution through hunting and destruction by rinderpest, the buffalo is plentiful in game reserves and national parks. Even today it does not appear to be a particularly endangered species. The same may be said of the common zebra, giraffe, and most of the antelope species of equatorial Africa.

Zebra

The zebra, although in places the staple food of lions, evidently has a high reproductive potential. Its bold stripes have been the subject of much discussion among students of animal coloration. Many capable naturalists, including Theodore Roosevelt, most of whom observed zebras in the nearly treeless plains of East Africa, claim that the markings are disadvantageous in that they make the animals conspicuous. At close range this is certainly true but, from a distance, the black and white bands merge together to form a light grey colour that is actually slightly less conspicuous than the dark colours of topi, tiang or wildebeest for example. In open country, the zebra does not need concealing coloration anyhow, for it is a gregarious animal and any enemy will soon be spotted by one or other of the herd. In close country or among scattered trees, however, the zebra is quite inconspicuous. As Raymond Cowles (1959) points out, it is in conditions such as this that the zebra is in the greatest danger and can best benefit from concealment.

This was the opinion, too, of Sir Percy Fitzpatrick, for he wrote 'Look at the zebra! There is nothing more striking, nothing arrests the eye more sharply—in the Zoo—than this vivid contrast of colour; yet in the bush the wavy stripes of black and white are a protection, enabling him to hide at will'.

It is clearly unwise to dogmatise about functional adaptations until an animal has been studied in all its habitats and in all the facets of its natural life.

Reptiles

There is a well known story in Herodotus that, in the temple of Athene on the Acropolis at Athens was the 'guardian' of the place, 'a great snake' which was regularly fed with honey cakes. When Athens was being evacuated at the time of the invasion of Xerxes, the snake's honey cake was left untouched and this was taken as a sign that the goddess herself had departed to accompany her people. Jennison suggests that the rodents which usually ate the cakes had probably been driven away by stress of hunger and that the snake had followed them!

A giant python, measuring 45 ft. in length, is said by Diodorus to have been captured in Ethiopia for Ptolemy II. It was taken alive to Alexandria, where it became tame and was kept on view at the royal palace. The Emperor Tiberius owned a large snake which he fed with his own hand and no doubt other Romans did likewise, but apart from those killed for food or for their skins, pythons have never been seriously molested by man.

Crocodiles were worshipped in Egypt from earliest times and were represented on monuments, coffins and papyri from the IV Dynasty to Ptolemaic times. Their most ancient representation as a hieroglyph appears on Nefermat's tomb near the IV Dynasty pyramid of Medum. Here Nefermat stands with one son before him while his wife and three other sons stand below. One of the latter is designated chief of the lake of the crocodile.

The Roman satirist Juvenal wrote scathingly, 'Who does not know what kinds of monsters dominated Egypt worship? One part adores the crocodile, another quakes before the ibis gorged with serpents . . . whole houses venerate cat, here a river-fish, and there a dog. . . .'. And Diodorus asked how it was that an animal which devoured man should receive the reverence paid to a deity. Like Cicero before him, he deduced that crocodiles must be a protection to the country. Without them, the people would have been pillaged from east or west, but invaders were deterred from swimming the Nile for fear of being devoured by the numerous saurians therein! This at least shows how plentiful crocodiles at one time were in Egypt.

Crocodiles were protected and preserved at towns such as Komombos, Thebes, Koptos and Crocodilopolis—Arsinoe in the Fayum. According to legend, their worship arose because Mona, first King of Egypt, was saved from his dogs that pursued him to Lake Moeris by a crocodile which carried him on its back to safety on the opposite bank. Later, the crocodile became the emblem of Sebek the water-god who caused the Nile to rise.

In other places, however, the crocodile was regarded as a symbol of impurity and an emblem of Typhon, and was therefore ruthlessly destroyed. As the impersonation of evil, a distinction that it shared with the lion and oryx, the crocodile was often represented under the feet of Horus, avenger of Osiris.

Crocodiles first appeared in the Roman amphitheatre in the shows of Scaurus in B.C. 58 when the first hippopotamus to be brought to Italy was exhibited with five crocodiles in a temporary pond. At the games of B.C. 2, 36 crocodiles were killed in a pool which had been made in the Circus Flaminius. These may have been the crocodiles which were accompanied to Rome by some men from Tentyra, near

Koptos. The crocodile, as a destroyer of garbage, was appreciated and revered in many parts of Egypt, but the Tentyrites had a great reputation for pursuing it relentlessly and fearlessly. A number of these men, said Strabo, went with some crocodiles to Rome and there gave a display of skill and courage. They entered the beasts' pond and dragged them in nets to the platforms for the spectators to see, before throwing them back into the water.[2] Crocodiles were also recorded at the shows of Antoninus Pius, Elagabalus (218-222 A.D.) and the praetorian Games of Symmachus in 401 A.D.

The ancient Egyptians were not the only people to worship crocodiles. In more recent times, some African tribes have done the same. For example, J. Bland-Sutton (1911) wrote: 'Some of the religions of the Sesse islanders [of Lake Victoria] were horrible. One of the gods (Kitinda) accepted no offering but men. The crocodile was his priest. When it was considered necessary to appease Kitinda, a man was hauled to the brink of the lake, where his kness and elbows were broken so that he could not crawl away. He was then abandoned and the crocodiles came and seized him. . . .'.

'The saying, by the way, of "crocodile tears" is nearly as common among the Arabs of the White Nile as with us, at least the origin of it; for they positively assert that the beast, having drowned his victim, tucks him under its arm, and carries him off to some lonely sandbank, where, previous to eating him, it sheds many tears of sorrow.'[3] It is now known from the work of Professor Knut Schmidt-Nielson[4] that the production of a saline solution from the nasal glands of reptiles and birds is a physiological mechanism for salt excretion. It is not improbable that the same may occur in crocodiles and account for their alleged tears.

As I pointed out in Chapter VI the crocodile is not nearly so dangerous to man as is generally supposed. Moreover it is a valuable and interesting member of the African fauna. Within recent years, however, the Nile crocodile has been drastically reduced in numbers. The main threat to its survival comes from modern methods employed by professional hunters who work at night in fast motor boats. The quarry is located in the beam of a powerful spotlight, shot at point-blank range and gaffed before it can sink. In reserves, crocodiles are poached with snares, baited hooks or harpoons and light in night operations from canoes.

Crocodiles are not detrimental to the fishing industry except where they damage fishing gear. Although they feed on fish during the middle years of life, a large proportion of the fish they eat are

[2]Jennison, 1937.
[3]Parkyns, 1853.
[4](1958), *Nature* **182,** 783-5.

either of secondary value or are themselves predatory species. Adult crocodiles also take a toll of otters, cormorants and darters. Destruction of crocodiles in Rhodesia was followed by a great increase in the numbers of otters and consequent damage to fisheries. In the Congo, predacious fishes multiplied when the crocodiles were reduced and, in Ceylon, the result was the elimination of smaller insect-eating fish and a consequent epidemic of malaria. In Madagascar, where the larger crocodiles often ate dogs and naturally tended to catch unhealthy animals, elimination of these natural destroyers of sick dogs resulted in an increase of rabies. It is difficult to foretell the effects of reducing animal numbers and thereby upsetting the balance of nature.

There are two main grounds for regarding the crocodile as a positive asset. First, it is a producer of high quality leather and, secondly, it is a tourist attraction. Under rational management, the reptiles could provide a sustained yield of skins and remain a lasting pleasure to tourists as well as to zoologists throughout the world.[5] As long as they are killed only after achieving sexual maturity and before they reach a dangerous old age, crocodiles will not be exterminated; nor will they be a danger to man.

[5]Cott, H. B. (1961) *Trans. Zool. Soc. Lond.* **29**, 211-337.

View on the banks of the Tacazzi. From H. Salt (1814).

CHAPTER X

GAME CONSERVATION

Though the largest of the continents, Africa has a human population of barely 200 million—half that of India and a third of that of China. Even so, the African population has probably doubled during the last century and, of those people living 100 years ago, at least a quarter were concentrated in Egypt and North Africa. Save for a few exceptionally well-favoured regions therefore, the country must then have been largely underpopulated with small, isolated communities gaining painful mastery of the all-devouring bush and not competing seriously with the wild life of the country.[1]

The real threat today to the wildlife of eastern Africa lies in the recent population increase which, of course, is merely part of the problem that faces the entire world. Unless some solution is achieved fairly soon, wild life will be doomed everywhere. But then, so will man. Personally, I do not believe in the early extinction of either. Since the time of Cecil Rhodes, Europeans have been either unduly optimistic or unduly pessimistic about Africa generally and about its wild life in particular. In this book I have tried to maintain a balance between the two extremes. An example of the pessimistic view is afforded by G. H. Hutchinson, who wrote as follows of the economic situation of Rhodesia in 1905: 'The mineral wealth of the country has fallen far short of expectations, and where it existed has in many cases been wasted by mismanagement. The farming has not yet recovered from the successive blows inflicted by the Matabele rebellion, the rinderpest, and the African coast fever; indeed the country cannot yet produce enough to feed the comparatively trifling population of some 12,000 people'. What a contrast to the prosperity of the country only 60 years later!

On the other hand, even today it would be unrealistic to expect further improvements in African economy without continued investment and research. At the same time, since it is becoming clearly apparent that the wild life of the continent has enormous economic potential, I think there are reasonable hopes that at least some of

[1]Oliver, 1961.

it may be preserved. In the final chapter, I shall indicate the potential importance of Africa's game animals.

Tourism

At a time when the world population explosion calls for the development and improvement of areas hitherto uninhabited or sparsely populated, it may seem paradoxical to maintain that the development of national parks and nature reserves is essential to the welfare of mankind. It must be remembered, however, that the aim of game conservation is not merely to preserve rare and unusual animals for the enjoyment of prosperity. It is to ensure that the land is put to its most economical and efficient use.

Tourism already provides Kenya's second largest source of income —nearly £10 million per year—and the total annual revenue from tourism throughout eastern Africa is very much higher. It could easily be increased from five to ten-fold within a few years: it is thus an extremely profitable form of land use. A combination of magnificent scenery with the world's finest wildlife together provide an irresistible attraction. Although some people would find virgin country without roads or hotels even more exciting, they do not, in this modern world, have the time and money for lengthy expeditions into the bush. In any case, there is now no choice. The wild life of eastern Africa has almost disappeared except where it is protected in national parks and game reserves.

It has been claimed that the income from tourism in natural areas of East Africa already brings a greater economic return per unit of an area than any other use to which the land could be put. Much of these areas is either so badly infested by tsetse flies or so arid as to be uneconomical from an agricultural point of view. At the same time, as we shall see, a meat crop can often be harvested from game which exceeds that available from livestock. Wildlife and tourism are therefore among the greatest economic assets of eastern Africa and national parks one of the land's most productive assets. For this reason, there are grounds for hoping that the opinions expressed in recent years, to the effect that even with conservation, certain of the larger game animals of Africa are doomed to early extinction, may be unduly pessimistic.

One aspect of tourism is big game hunting. Although this is a sport for the rich and only about one per cent of visitors to eastern Africa can indulge in it, nevertheless, it should also be encouraged as a form of land use, in conjunction with ordinary tourism and game cropping. It is not necessarily detrimental to the fauna since the animals shot by hunters are almost invariably males past breeding age and carrying large tusks or horns. Moreover, there are strict limits to the number of animals that may be killed on licence and, in fact, the most ardent sportsmen are naturally anxious to conserve and protect the game. Probably about 10,000 head are killed annually throughout East Africa by resident and visiting hunters. Yet this industry alone yields over £500,000 per year.[2]

Game Cropping

As I have already mentioned, game animals can withstand a good deal of cropping by human predators. As long ago as 1860, Sir Richard Burton wrote: 'The elephant roams in herds throughout the country, affecting the low grounds where stagnating water produces a plentiful vegetation: with every human being its foe, and thousands living by its destruction, the animal is far from becoming scarce; indeed, the greatest number of footprints appeared near Chogwe and Tongwe, stations of Baloch garrisons close to the town of Panyani'. But he also said: 'The fauna appear to be rare upon the banks of the Tanganyika: all men are hunters; every human being loves animal food, from white ants to elephants; the tzetze was found there, and probably the luxuriance of the vegetation, in conjunction with the extreme humidity, tends to diminish species and individuals. Herds of elephants exist in the bamboo-jungles which surround the sea, but the heaps of ivory sold in the markets of Ujiji are collected from an area containing thousands of square miles'.

The game carrying capacity of an area is the maximum number or mass of animals that can be sustained by the environment for an indefinite period—that is, without overgrazing. While often measured in numbers of animals per unit area, a more useful expression of carrying capacity probably is the total weight or *biomass*.

This idea was actually almost suggested by W. J. Burchell as early as 1824 when he wrote: 'As far as I am enabled to judge, there is no region in any quarter of the world which can hold competition with *Southern Africa* in number of large animals. It would be a novel and not uninstructive mode of comparing the *zoology* of different countries by noting the aggregate weight of the wild animals of each country (meaning one individual of each species) divided by the total number of species. If a table of this kind were formed, I think there is little doubt that Southern Africa would be found to stand at the head of it'.

Biomass varies according to the species supported and many other factors, so that figures of productivity must always be treated with caution. For example, both hippopotamus and elephant are long-lived species, so that their nutritional requirements per unit weight

[2]A. B. Adams (ed.) (1962) *First World Conference on National Parks*. Washington D.C.: U.S. Department of the Interior.

on a population maintenance basis are doubtless lower than for a corresponding biomass of smaller and shorter-lived species. A somewhat lower carrying capacity would presumably prevail if only hippopotamuses and elephants were present.

It is also likely that hippos, in transferring plant nutrients from land to water, cause an accelerated rate of depletion of the habitat. This is probably a more serious loss than would be true for a population of entirely terrestrial species whose defaecations would be retained within the soil structure. On this basis, the carrying capacity biomass of 100,000 lbs. per square mile in Queen Elizabeth Park, Uganda, may be an underestimate.[3] Nevertheless, it is about four times as high as the biomass carrying capacity for the plains game ungulates of Kenya or for the best natural livestock ranges in the western United States.

The highest biomass density recorded anywhere in the world is 125,000 lbs. per square mile around Lake Manyara, Tanganyika: but it is not yet known whether this is constant throughout the year nor whether it exceeds the long-term carrying capacity of the land. It may be the result of the compression and confinement of the elephant and buffalo that, until recently, occupied a much larger range.[4]

Not only can a higher biomass be attained per unit area by a number of mammal species exploiting a wide range of natural vegetation, but the presence of a large number of species is an insurance against plagues, pestilence and other natural disasters. For, whereas some species may be particularly vulnerable to one disease, others may be resistant to that and susceptible to another. A mixture of species provides a wide spectrum of resistance. At the same time the population of any one species is never particularly high and consequently epidemic diseases are not likely to spread through it very rapidly. Yet another advantage of maintaining mixed populations lies in the fact that species are preserved which, although not at present known to be useful or interesting may, at some future date, become invaluable in some unforeseen way. For example, they might be found to feed on particularly noxious weeds, like water hyacinth, and thus be useful in control measures.

Let us now consider why wild game populations are so much more productive in terms of biomass than are domestic animals. First, through many generations of intensive natural selection, they have become well adapted to their environment. For example, buffalo can thrive on natural grasses that will not even maintain the weight of native cattle. They also show larger gains in weight than African

[3]Petrides, G. A. & Swank, W. G. (1965) *Zool. Afric.* **1**, 209-25.
[4]Watson, R. M. & Turner, M. I. M. (1965) *E. Afr. Wildl. J.* **3**, 95-8.

or European cattle on most forms of natural vegetation. This may be because domestic cattle tend to suffer from various physiological disadvantages. In particular, among European breeds hair length is controlled by the duration of daylight. The short 12-hour tropical day engenders long 'winter' coats. The animals are unable to adapt themselves to warm climates and lose condition to a remarkable degree. In parts of East Africa, the waters contain quantities of fluorine lethal to domestic cattle but which do not appear to affect the local wild game. Again, several antelope species have become so well adapted to aridity that they thrive on a water ration wholly inadequate for cattle or even camels.

Secondly, it is regarded as axiomatic that no two distinct species can occupy exactly the same environment and make identical demands upon it. On the other hand, in different habitats similar ecological niches may be occupied by quite unrelated species. Thus, of all the game animals of eastern Africa, each is making a slightly different demand of the environment or is affecting it in a slightly different way. This means that the habitat is never stocked to the capacity of any one species. Use of vegetation is thorough, without being excessive, and the risk of soil erosion consequently reduced.

Not only are individual wild species intrinsically more productive than sheep and cattle but, in nature, there is a three-dimensional utilization of the vegetation which is more efficient than a single crop at ground level eaten by a couple of species of domestic animals. The wild pig will exploit roots and bulbs, smaller antelopes the grasses. Large forms feed on bushes whilst elephants and giraffe eat from the tops of trees. In order to obtain the highest yield, the whole fauna should be rationally conserved and exploited.

Another argument in favour of wild game rather than domestic animals as producers of protein for human food lies in the fact that the latter are more susceptible to disease, especially trypanosomiasis, than are game animals but, at the same time, they are more attractive to tsetse flies. In many parts of eastern Africa, as we have seen, instead of exploiting the natural resistance of game animals, tsetse control methods have employed operations designed to exterminate them.

Wild animals undoubtedly build up immunity to various forms of disease and it is probably even an advantage for them to be subjected to epizootic diseases at regular intervals. If, for example, a region is kept clear of rinderpest for a number of years and then becomes infected, the casualty rate is very much higher. Some years ago in Kenya, there was an unfortunate mistake in the application of protective vaccine which caused an outbreak of rinderpest in cattle instead of preventing it. This caused a 90 per cent mortality of the eland in the nature reserves. Had these been subjected to minor infections regularly, no doubt greater resistance would have been acquired.[5]

One of the objections to game cropping, as opposed to cattle ranching, has been the difficulties that arise in finding efficient techniques for slaughtering the various species, developing practicable techniques for preserving the meat, assessing the potential market, fulfilling public health requirements and so on. Nevertheless, research is now in progress in several countries of eastern Africa that should shed light on these problems.[6] Here, I will mention only one that is of a purely technical nature.

The use of heavy calibre sporting rifles for elephant cropping is most inefficient because it causes considerable disturbance to other animals. Animals that have been wounded become aggressive and dangerous and others shy and vindictive. A far better method is to use a cross-bow firing a dart syringe containing a lethal dose of narcotic drugs. If the target animal is approached, unobserved in daylight, this technique has the obvious advantage of silence, absence of the requirements of extreme accuracy and elimination of the typical reactions of an animal wounded by rifle fire, even from a fatal heart or lung shot.

It is humane for it is impossible to wound or lose an animal darted with an overdose of succinyl-choline chloride and the meat of animals killed this way is perfectly edible as the drug is destroyed by heat and not effective when taken by mouth.[7] The same technique can be used for buffalo, eland, giraffe and other ungulates, while smaller antelope such as impala are hunted from blinds with a light rifle fitted with telescopic sights.

For game cropping, some of the most deadly tricks of the professional poacher are often the most satisfactory. Thus if game are sniped from cover in such a way that they do not see or smell the hunters, large numbers can be killed without the others becoming greatly disturbed. The noise of firearms alone, and especially of small calibre weapons not associated with the presence of man, causes only temporary alarm. As Prof. R. F. Dasmann (1946) points out, if blinds are constructed near drinking places, where the game comes in during the dry season, large numbers can be obtained by continued shooting.

Night-hunting, using powerful lights such as the headlights of a car, confuses animals and makes them extremely easy to shoot, but does not greatly disturb the herds. It is because night-hunting and

[5]Cowie, M. (1958) *Mammalia* **22,** 427-34.
[6]Feely, J. M. (1965) *Zool. Afric.* **1,** 227-230.
[7]Pienaar, U. de V. & Niekerk, J. W. van (1963) *Oryx* **7,** 35-8.

shooting from blinds are so deadly that they are illegal. But game laws are intended to protect the game. If the game is being ranched on an economic, scientific basis further safeguards are not required. The aim is to obtain meat, not sport, and the most efficient methods should therefore be employed.

Successful game conservation is complicated, too, by the natural tendency of wild animals to wander from national parks and reserves, and to raid crops in adjacent agricultural land. In the long run, the only satisfactory answer to this problem lies in the erection of physical barriers. Unfortunately, this is extremely expensive, as a fence must be very strong to contain large game such as elephants, although a fence of elevator cables fixed to sections of old tramline has proved satisfactory. Nevertheless, 'the ingenuity, versatility, determination and intelligence of elephant (and buffalo, although to a lesser degree) cannot be underestimated'. A successful game ditch can divide virgin forest with its concentration of wild game that reaps considerable yearly profit from equally profitable, highly productive farm land whose crops are also of vital economic importance. Experiments in the Aberdare Forests of Kenya have shown the most successful barrier to be a sloped ditch, extra deep at the bottom, presenting a 7 to 8 foot outside bank or wall, topped with an angled wire fence. Such a ditch, however, requires constant maintenance which must be carried out by hand labour where the country cannot be negotiated by machinery.[8]

The advantages and disadvantages of velt burning in Africa are controversial subjects. Large numbers of beautiful trees are destroyed or damaged so that they become vulnerable to bacteriological infection, woodboring insects and further onslaughts by fire. Naturally the least fire resistant species are affected most severely, so that they become eliminated by competition. On the other hand, fire and grazing throughout the world are largely responsible for producing and maintaining grassland as we have seen (p. 5), and it seems probable that controlled burning is necessary in game reserves for a number of reasons.

Where there is undergrazing because the fauna is restricted through the scarcity or lack of water, burning is the only practical method of removing surplus dry plant matter which would otherwise inhibit the growth of fresh grass. Without enough grazing or burning, the bush tends to encroach so that the game-carrying capacity of the land decreases. Furthermore, controlled burning is one way of minimising the frequency of accidental fires which are even more destructive.

Consequently, a programme of three-year rotational burning,

[8]Woodley, F. W. (1965) E. Afr. Wildl. J. 3, 89-94.

achieved by the construction of fire breaks, has resulted in great improvement on the burning policies of the past. Areas damaged by drought are temporarily excluded whilst the catchment areas of springs and rivers are, for obvious reasons, never burned.[9]

Accessibility to water dominates the tropical African scene and adequate water supplies are necessary for game conservation. Many large areas of pasture land do not carry their full weight of game animals simply because of water-shortage. The construction of water points, too, can check major seasonal migrations even though the animals instinctively become somewhat restless around the areas in which they stay. When the whole countryside was teeming with game, local droughts were not disastrous. Today, they tend to be very dangerous unless water is supplied artificially, if they occur in one of the small pockets in which the wild fauna persists. In 1910 the Athai plains were so dry that zebras came right into Nairobi in their search for water and lions nightly killed game in the open square in the centre of the town.

The devastating effects of local drought are well illustrated by the following quotation from J. W. Gregory's book, *The Great Rift Valley* (1896). 'Here and there around a water hole we found acres of ground white with the bones of rhinoceros and zebra, gazelle and antelope, jackal and hyaena, and among them we once observed the remains of a lion. All the bones of the skeletons were there, and they were fresh and ungnawed. The explanation is simple. The year before there had been a drought, which had cleared both game and people from the district. Those which did not migrate crowded round the dwindling pools, and fought for the last drop of water'.

It is, however, often difficult and expensive to provide and maintain artificial water points, especially where the subterranean water is saline. Furthermore, to concentrate game around water may encourage poaching and also be detrimental to the pasture. An alternative is to provide shade in the remote parts of isolated plains, because many species of game animals feeding in green pasture seldom need to drink, even during the hot season, if they have access to shade. Isolated trees should be preserved and, if possible, extended to form natural groves. The more scattered these are, the harder it will be for poachers to ambush the animals under them and the less will be the grazing pressure extended on the surrounding pasture.[10]

The world has lost over 100 kinds of animals and innumerable birds, reptiles and other animals during the last 2,000 years. Without national parks and nature reserves, these numbers would be very

[9]Brynard, A. M. pp. 371-93 *in* Davis, D. H. S., 1964.
[10]Vesey-Fitzgerald, D. F. (1960) *J. Mammal.* **41**, 161-72.

much greater. Extermination may be direct, through killing, or indirect by the changing of natural habitats. A species of plant or animal does not exist independently, but is part of a complex habitat web[11] which may be destroyed by cultivation, flooding, drainage, urbanization, or the grazing of domestic livestock. An important reason for nature conservation is to provide material for ecological research. There can be few environments left in the world that are unaffected by mankind. As I have constantly pointed out, the survival of many animal species is connected with human intervention. Nevertheless, a strict nature reserve provides an important control for comparison with otherwise similar areas in which the environment is deliberately modified.

It has been argued that strict preservation in national parks results in overgrazing and destruction of the environment. To some extent this is true: as I mentioned earlier, the big game of Africa evolved a form of natural symbiosis with the indigenous human population. On the other hand, the abundance of elephants and hippopotamuses in certain reserves has been caused partly by the immigration of animals from surrounding areas where they enjoy no protection. Strict preservation of areas such as this would require their enclosure to prevent these animals from getting in. In many cases, therefore, the slaughter of excess animals merely comes to the same thing as restoring the equilibrium unbalanced by human activity. Moreover, only in strict reserves, preferably situated in the hearts of national parks, can the psychologist study the natural behaviour of the higher vertebrates. In assessing the economics of nature conservation, its scientific importance should not be neglected.

Conservation of the fauna, therefore, does not imply merely preserving big game for the pleasure of hunters and the delight of tourists—economically profitable though these aspects may also be. Essentially it is a way of land management and development. Thus, if natural predators such as lions are reduced in numbers the herbivores must be controlled by shooting in order to prevent over-grazing.

In many countries, unfortunately, official policy still seems to regard the natural fauna as something to be destroyed or fenced off in reserves where it can do no harm. Biologists, however, know how complicated may be the relationships of an ecosystem and that destruction of a single species may upset the whole pattern of a region.

In the old days the Masai regarded the stock of wild game as a measure of protection for their cattle. Lions tended to move with the game and live on it in preference to the domestic herds. Nor

[11]Cloudsley-Thompson, 1965.

were they particularly harmful to the game since they mostly killed the surplus young, the old and the sick.

Not only is a degree of predation beneficial to animal populations, a point that I have discussed in detail in my book *Animal Conflict and Adaptation* (1965), but even ruthless killers such as hunting-dogs (*Lycaon pictus*) are frequently useful in arranging for new blood to be introduced. For example, a herd of impala may be dominated and served by one male for a number of years with consequent inbreeding. Hunting-dogs go through and cause such havoc that many large herds split up and join new males.

There are three main reasons for the conservation of the natural fauna. The first is to provide material for research purposes, in particular with regard to ascertaining the economic potential of the land. The second is purely economic; because the natural fauna has been selected over such a long period that it is inevitably more productive than introduced, exotic forms. Finally, the conservation of variety is an insurance against ecological imbalance with the attendant risk of pestilence, plagues and soil erosion.

To achieve these desirable aims, Dr. E. B. Worthington[12] has recommended that strict nature reserves, maintained for scientific study under conditions of no interference with natural processes, should be situated within national parks. The latter, managed to provide a maximum carrying capacity for wild animals and maximum attraction to tourists should, in turn, be surrounded by buffer zones. These would likewise be managed with an eye to maximum sustained yield of wild animals, derived both from the buffer zone itself and from the overflow from the national park, and would be cropped by legalized hunters. In settled areas surrounding the buffer zone, those kinds of wild animals which cause damage would be strongly discouraged.

During the last few years it has become generally accepted that planned cropping of wild ungulates may be the most efficient and economical way of using many vast marginal areas of eastern Africa where cattle ranching and cultivation are unwise or impossible. Countries in which this type of land occurs are therefore beginning to count themselves fortunate if they have managed to preserve some of their indigenous big game to provide a nucleus for future expansion.

[12](1960), *Oryx* **5,** 341-5.

APPENDIX I

The following is a list of some of the more famous big game hunters and explorers of eastern Africa.

Akeley, C.
Anderson, G. H.
Baker, S. W.
Baldwin, W. C.
Banks, F. G.
Barnes, J. H.
Bell, W. D. M.
Black, A.
Blaine, G.
Buckley, W.
Burchell, W. J.
Burton, R. F.
Caldwell, K.
Campbell, J. S.
Cannone, E.
Chaillu, P. B. du
Chapman, A.
Christy, C.
Clarke, F. M.
Cunningham, R. J.
Dunbar, J.
Emin Pasha (E. Schnitzer)
Fairweather, R. G.
Faulkner, H.
Finaughty, W.
Fitzpatrick, P.
Fletcher, O.
Foá, E.
Gibbons, A. St. H.
Gordon, R. W.
Gordon-Cumming, R. G.
Gray, G.
Grogan, E. S.
Harris, W. Cornwallis
Hartley, H.
Hatton, D. F.
Hobley, C. W.
Hunter, J. A.
Jackson, F. J.

Jacobs, Petrus
James, F. L.
Johnson, H. H.
Judd, W.
Kirby, F. L.
Kittenberger, K.
Kruger, C.
Laborie, B. de
Lacerda, de
Livingstone, D.
Loder, E.
Lyell, D. D.
Lyell, J. C.
Maugham, R. C. F.
Millais, J. G.
Mostyn, P.
Neumann, A. H.
Oswell, W. C.
Pearson, P.
Pease, A. E.
Phillips, L.
Pitman, C. S. R.
Powell-Cotton, P. H. G.
Pretorious, P. J.
Reel, B.
Ritchie, A. T. A.
Rooyen, C. van
Ryan, M.
Salmon, R. T. D.
Selous, F. C.
Sharpe, A.
Speke, J. H.
Stanley, H. M.
Statham, J. C. B.
Steidman, A.
Steinacher, L.
Stephens, F. T.
Stevenson-Hamilton, J.
Stigand, C. H.

Stockley, V. M.
Sutherland, J.
Swartz, M.
Swynnerton, C. M. F.
Tarlton, L. J.
Teare, P.

Teleki, S. von Szek
Temple-Perkins, E. A.
Varion, H. F.
Viljoen, J. van
Wolhieter, H. C.

APPENDIX II

Biomass of the main wild mammalian species in a number of areas.[1]

Area	Authority	Biomass (Metric tons per km²)
Ruanda-Ruchure plain Parc National Albert, Congo (11 spp.)	F. Bouliére and J. Verschuren	24.4
Queen Elizabeth National Park, Uganda	R. Bere	19.5
Nairobi National Park, Kenya	S. I. Ellis	15.6
Serengeti Plains, Tanganyika	B. Grzimek	5.2
Henderson Ranch, S. Rhodesia (16 spp.)	R. F. Dasmann and A. S. Mossman	4.9
Kruger National Park, Transvaal	R. Knobel	1.8
Scottish Deer Forest (Red Deer)	V. P. W. Lowe	1.0
Canadian Barren Grounds (Caribou)	A. W. F. Banfield	0.8
Southern Russia (Saiga Antelope)	A. Bannikov	0.35

[1]From Huxley, J. (1962) *Endeavour* **21**, 98-107.

BIBLIOGRAPHY

The following is a list of the more important works consulted. English translations have been cited, in preference to original foreign language editions, as the former have been used as sources for quotations.

Ahlefeldt Bille, G. (1951). *Tandalla.* (Trans. from the Danish by H. Young.) London: Routledge & Kegan Paul.

Andersson, C. J. (2nd ed.) (1856). *Lake Ngami.* London: Hurst & Blackett. (Copyright: Hutchinson.)

Baker, S. W. (1866). *The Albert N'Yanza, Great Basin of the Nile.* (2 Vols.) London: Macmillan.

Baker, S. W. (1867). *The Nile Tributaries of Abyssinia.* London: Macmillan.

Baker, S. W. (1890). *Wild Beasts and their Ways.* (2 Vols.) London: Macmillan.

Baldwin, W. C. (1863). *African Hunting—from Natal to the Zambesi.* London: Richard Bentley.

Barrow, J. (1801-4). *Travels into the Interior of Southern Africa in the years 1797 and 1798.* (2 Vols.) London: T. Cadell and W. Davies.

Bell, W. D. M. (1923). *Wanderings of an Elephant Hunter.* London: Country Life.

Bell, W. D. M. (1949). *Karamojo Safari.* London: Gollancz.

Bell, W. D. M. (1960). *Bell of Africa.* London: Holland Press.

Bellefonds, Linant de (1958). (Ed. M. Shinnie.) *Journal d'un Voyage à Méroé dans les Années 1821 et 1822.* Khartoum: Sudan Antiquities Service.

Bland-Sutton, J. (1911). *Man and Beast in Eastern Ethiopia.* London: Macmillan.

Blunt, D. E. (1933). *Elephant.* London: East Africa Press.

Briggs, L. C. (1960). *Tribes of the Sahara.* Cambridge, Mass.: Harvard Univ. Press.

Brocklehurst, H. C. (1931). *Game Animals of the Sudan.* London: Gurney and Jackson.

Browne, W. G. (1799). *Travels in Africa, Egypt, and Syria.* London: T. Cadell jr., W. Davies; and T. N. Longman & O. Rees.

Bruce, J. (1790). *Travels to discover the Source of the Nile in the years 1768-1773.* (5 Vols.) Edinburgh and London: Robinson.

Buckley, W. (1933). *Big Game Hunting in Central Africa.* London: Palmer.

Burchell, W. J. (1822, 1824). *Travels in the Interior of Southern Africa.* (2 Vols.) London: Longman, Hurst, Rees, Orme & Browne.

Burton, R. F. (1856). *First Footsteps in East Africa.* London: Dent.

Burton, R. F. (1860). *The Lake Region of Central Africa*. (2 Vols.) London: Longman, Green, Longman & Roberts.

Cameron, V. L. (1877). *Across Africa*. (2 Vols.) London: Philip.

Campbell, J. (1815). *Travels in South Africa*. London: Black & Parry.

Carrington, R. (1958). *Elephants*. London: Chatto & Windus.

Casati, G. (1891). *Ten Years in Equatoria*. (2 Vols.) (Trans. J. R. Clay.) London: Frederick Warne.

Chaillu, P. B. du (1861). *Explorations and Adventures in Equatorial Africa*. London: John Murray.

Chanler, W. A. (1896). *Through Jungle and Desert. Travels in Eastern Africa*. London: Macmillan.

Christy, C. (1924). *Big Game and Pygmies*. London: Macmillan.

Churi, J. H. (1853). *Sea Nile, the Desert and Nigritia*. London: Published by the Author.

Cloudsley-Thompson, J. L. (1960). *Animal Behaviour*. Edinburgh: Oliver and Boyd.

Cloudsley-Thompson, J. L. (1965). *Animal Conflict and Adaptation*. London: Foulis.

Cosson, E. A. de (1877). *The Cradle of the Blue Nile*. (2 Vols.) London: John Murray.

Cowles, R. B. (1959). *Zulu Journal*. Berkeley: Univ. California Press.

Cronwright-Schreiner, S. G. (1925). *The Migratory Springbucks of South Africa*. London: Fisher Unwin. (Copyright: Ernest Benn.)

Cureau, A. L. (1915). *Savage Man in Central Africa*. (Trans. by E. Andrews.) London: Fisher Unwin.

Daly, M. (1937). *Big Game Hunting and Adventure 1897-1936*. London: Macmillan.

Dane, R. M. (1921). *Sport in Africa and Asia*. London: Andrew Melrose.

Darley, H. (1926). *Slaves and Ivory*. London: Witherby.

Dasmann, R. F. (1964). *African Game Ranching*. Oxford: Pergamon.

Davis, D. H. S. (Ed.) (1964). Ecological Studies in Southern Africa. *Monogr. Biol.* **14,** 1-415.

Debenham, F. (1955). *Nyasaland*. London: H.M.S.O.

Denham, D. and Clapperton, H. (1826). *Narrative of Travels and Discoveries in Northern and Central Africa*. London: John Murray.

Denman, E. (1957). *Animal Africa*. London: Robert Hale.

Dugmore, A. Radcliffe (1928). *African Jungle Life*. London: Macmillan.

Elliot, G. F. S. (1896). *A Naturalist in Mid-Africa*. London: A. D. Innes.

Elton, J. F. (1879). *The Lakes and Mountains of Eastern and Central Africa*. (Ed. H. B. Cotterill.) London: John Murray.

Emin (1888). *Emin Pasha in Central Africa*. (Ed. G. Schweinfurth *et al.*) (Trans. Mrs. R. W. Filkin.) London: George Philip.

Fage, J. D., and Oliver R. (1962). *A Short History of Africa*. Harmondsworth, Midd.: Penguin.

Fife, C. W. Domville (1927). *Savage Life in the Black Sudan*. London: Seeley, Service.

Fitzpatrick, D. (1907). *Jock of the Bushveld*. London: Longmans Green.

Fitzsimons, F. W. (1919). *The Natural History of South Africa.* (4 Vols.) London: Longmans Green.

Foá, E. (1899). *After Big Game in Central Africa.* (Trans. from the French by F. Lees.) London: Black.

Fothergill, E. (1910). *Five years in the Sudan.* London: Hurst & Blackett.

Frazer, J. (1922). *Episodes of my Life.* London: Macmillan.

Frazer, J. G. (1894). *The Golden Bough.* (2 Vols.) London: Macmillan. (Copyright: Trinity College, Cambridge, and A. P. Watt.)

Frederick, The Duke Adolphus (1910). *In the Heart of Africa.* (Trans. G. E. Maberley-Oppler.) London: Cassell.

Gibbons, A. St H. (1904). *Africa from South to North through Marotseland.* (2 Vols.) London: John Lane.

Gordon, C. G. (1881). *Colonel Gordon in Central Africa 1874-1879.* (Ed. G. B. Hill.) London: Thos. de la Rue.

Gordon-Cumming, R. G. (1850). *Five Years of a Hunter's Life in the far Interior of South Africa.* London: John Murray.

Gregory, J. W. (1896). *The Great Rift Valley.* London: John Murray.

Grogan, E. S. and Sharp, A. H. (1900). *From the Cape to Cairo.* London: Hurst & Blackett. (Copyright: Hutchinson.)

Grzimek, B. and M. (1960). *Serengeti shall not die.* (Trans. from the German by E. L. and D. Rewald.) London: Hamish Hamilton.

Guggisberg, C. A. W. (1961). *Simba.* Cape Town: Howard Timmins.

H. W. (1934). . . . . *something new out of Africa.* London: Pitmans. Pitmans.

Harris, W. Cornwallis (1844). *The Highlands of AEthiopia.* (2 Vols.) London: Longman, Brown, Green & Longmans.

Heape, W. (1931). *Emigration, Migration and Nomadism.* Cambridge: W. Heffer.

Hediger, H. (1955). *Studies of the Psychology and Behaviour of Captive Animals in Zoos and Circuses.* London: Butterworths.

Hodson, A. (n.d.c. 1929.) *Where Lion reign.* London: Skeffington.

Höhnel, L. von (1894). *Discovery of Lakes Rudolf and Stefanie.* (Trans. N. Bell.) (2 Vols.) London: Longmans, Green.

Hoskins, G. A. (1835). *Travels in Ethiopia.* London: Longman, Rees, Orme, Brown, Green & Longmans.

Hutchinson, G. H. (1905). *From the Cape to the Zambesi.* London: John Murray.

Huxley, E. (1964). *Forks and Hope. An African Notebook.* London: Chatto & Windus.

Jack, E. M. (1914). *On the Congo Frontier. Exploration and Sport.* London: Fisher Unwin.

Jackson, F. J. et al (1894). *Big Game Shooting.* (2 Vols.) London: Badminton Library.

James, F. L. (1883). *The Wild Tribes of the Soudan.* London: John Murray.

Jeannin, A. (1947). *L'Eléphant d'Afrique; Zoologie, Histoire, Folklore, Chasse, Protection.* Paris: Payot.

Jennison, G. (1937). *Animals for Show and Pleasure in Ancient Rome.* Manchester: Univ. Press.

Johnston, H. H. (1897). *British Central Africa*. London: Methuen.

Johnston, H. H. (1910). *Britain across the Seas. Africa*. London: National Society.

Junker, W. (1892). *Travels in Africa during the years 1882-1886*. (Trans. from the German by A. H. Keane.) London: Chapman & Hall.

Kerr, W. M. (1886). *The far Interior*. (2 Vols.) London: Sampson Low, Marston, Searle & Rivington.

Kingsley, M. H. (1897). *Travels in West Africa*. London. Macmillan.

Kittenberger, K. (1929). *Big Game Hunting and Collecting in East Africa 1903-26*. London: E. Arnold.

Kollmann, P. (1899). *The Victoria Nyanza*. London: Swan Sonnenschein.

Krapf, J. L. (1860). *Travels, Researches and Missionary Labours during Eighteen Years' Residence in Eastern Africa*. London: Trübner.

Landor, A. H. S. (1907). *Across widest Africa*. (2 Vols.) London: Hurst and Blackett. (Copyright: Hutchinson.)

Leakey, L. S. B. (1951). *Olduvai Gorge*. Cambridge: Univ. Press.

Legh, T. (1816). *Narrative of a Journey in Egypt*. London: Murray.

Le Vaillant, F. (1790). *Voyage dans l'Intérieur de l'Afrique dans les Années 1780-85*. (3 Vols.) (Ed. C. Varon.) Paris: Leroy, Jansen.

Livingstone, D. (1857). *Missionary Travels and Researches in South Africa*. (2 Vols.) London: John Murray.

Livingstone, D. (1874). *The last Journals of David Livingstone in Central Africa from 1865 to his death*. (2 Vols.) (Ed. H. Waller.) London: John Murray.

Livingstone, D. and C. (1865). *Narrative of an Expedition to the Zambezi and its Tributaries*. London: John Murray.

Lloyd, A. B. (1906). *Uganda to Khartoum*. London: Fisher Unwin.

Loisel, G. (1812). *Histoire des Ménageries de l'Antiquité à nos Jours*. (3 Vols.) Paris: Laurens.

Long, C. Chaillé (1876). *Central Africa: Naked Truths of Naked People*. London: Sampson Low, Marston, Searle & Rivington.

Lydekker, R. (1926). (2nd Ed. revised by J. G. Dollman.) *The Game Animals of Africa*. London: Roland Ward.

Lyell, D. D. (1924). *The African Elephant and its Hunters*. London: Heath Cranton.

Maugham, R. C. F. (1910). *Zambezia*. London: John Murray.

Melladew, H. (1909). *Sport and Travel Papers*. London, Fisher Unwin.

Melland, F. (1938). *Elephants in Africa*. London: Country Life.

Millais, J. G. (1899). *A Breath from the Veldt*. London: Henry Sotheran.

Millais, J. G. (1924). *Far away up the Nile*. London: Longmans Green.

Moorehead, A. (1959). *No Room in the Ark*. London: Hamish Hamilton. (Copyright: Laurence Pollinger.)

Murray, H. (1817). *Historical Account of Discoveries and Travels in Africa by the late John Leyden, M.D.* (2 Vols.) Edinburgh: Constable.

Ness, B. (1929). *Ten Thousand Miles in two Continents*. London: Methuen.

Neumann, A. H. (1898). *Elephant Hunting in East Equatorial Africa.* London: Roland Ward.

Nicholson, G. (1848). *The Cape and its Colonists.* London: Henry Colburn.

Oates, F. (1881). *Matabeleland and the Victoria Falls.* (Ed. C. G. Oates.) London: Kegan Paul, Trench.

Oberjohann, H. (1953). *Wild Elephant Chase.* London: D. Dobson.

Oliver, R. (ed.) (1961). *The Dawn of African History.* London: Oxford Univ. Press.

Parke, T. H. (1891). *My personal Experiences in Equatorial Africa.* London: Sampson Low, Marston.

Parkyns, M. (1853). *Life in Abyssinia.* (2 Vols.) London: John Murray.

Patterson, J. H. (1907). *The Man-Eaters of Tsavo.* London: Macmillan.

Patterson, J. H. (1909). *In the Grip of the Nyika.* London: Macmillan.

Pease, A. E. (1913). *The Book of the Lion.* London: John Murray.

Petherick, J. (1861). *Egypt, the Soudan and Central Africa.* Edinburgh: William Blackwood.

Petherick, Mr. and Mrs. (1869). *Travels in Central Africa.* (2 Vols.) London: Tinsley Bros.

Pliny (1601). *The Historie of the World. Commonly called the Natuarell Historie of C. Plinius Secundus.* (Trans. into English by Phaleman Holland) London: A. Islip.

Portal, G. (1894). *The British Mission to Uganda in 1893.* London: E. Arnold.

van der Post, L. (1958). *The lost World of the Kalahari.* London: Hogarth.

Powell-Cotton, P. H. G. (1902). *A Sporting Trip through Abyssinia.* London: Roland Ward.

Ritter, E. A. (1955). *Shaka Zulu.* London: Longmans.

Roedelberger, F. A. and Grosehoff, V. I. (1964). *African Wildlife.* (English version by N. O'Leary and P. Paulet.) London: Constable.

Salt, H. (1814). *A Voyage to Abyssinia.* London: Rivington.

Schweinfurth, G. (1873). *The Heart of Africa.* (Trans. E. E. Frewer.) (2 Vols.) London: Sampson Low, Marston, Low & Searle.

Scully, W. C. (1898). *Between Sun and Sand: a Tale of an African Desert.* London: Methuen.

Selous, F. C. (1881). *A Hunter's Wanderings in Africa.* London: Richard Bentley. (Later editions Macmillan.)

Selous, F. C. (1893). *Travel and Adventure in South-East Africa.* London: Roland Ward.

Shaw, T. (1738). *Travels or Observations relating to Several Parts of Barbary and the Levant.* Oxford: Printed at the Theatre.

Southworth, A. S. (1875). *Four thousand Miles of African Travel.* New York: Baker, Pratt.

Sparrman, A. (1785). *A Voyage to the Cape of Good Hope towards the Antarctic Polar Circle and round the World but chiefly into the Country of the Hottentots and Caffres, from the year 1772-1776.* (Trans. from the Swedish original by George Forster.) (2 Vols.) Perth: Morison.

Speke, J. H. (1863). *Journal of the Discovery of the Source of the Nile.* Edinburgh: William Blackwood.

Speke, J. H. (1864). *What led to the Discovery of the Source of the Nile.* Edinburgh: William Blackwood.

Stanley, H. M. (1872). *How I found Livingstone. Travels, Adventures, and Discoveries in Central Africa.* London: Sampson Low, Marston, Low & Searle.

Stanley, H. M. (1878). *Through the dark Continent.* (2 Vols.) London: Sampson, Low, Marston, Searle & Rivington.

Stanley, H. M. (1890). *In darkest Africa.* London: Sampson, Low, Marston, Searle & Rivington.

Stevenson-Hamilton, J. (1912). *Animal Life in Africa.* London: Heinemann.

Stigand, C. H. (1913). *Hunting the Elephant in Africa.* London: Macmillan.

Street, P. (1961). *Vanishing Animals: Preserving Nature's Rarities.* London: Faber & Faber.

Swann, A. J. (1910). *Fighting the Slave Hunters in Central Africa.* London: Seeley.

Sykes, C. A. (1903). *Service and Sport on the tropical Nile.* London: John Murray.

Tabler, E. G. (1955). *The far Interior. Chronicles of Pioneering in the Matabele and Mashona Countries, 1847-79.* Cape Town: Balkema.

Temple-Perkins, E. A. (1955). *Kingdom of the Elephant.* London: Andrew Melrose.

Thomson, J. (1885). *Through Masai Land.* London: Sampson, Low, Marston, Searle & Rivington.

Topsell, E. (1658). *History of Four footed Beasts and Serpents . . . Whereunder is now added the Theater of Insects; by T. Muffet.* (Revised by J. R.) London.

Wallace, H. F. (1934). *Big Game Wanderings in Many Lands.* London: Eyre & Spottiswoode.

Wellby, M. S. (1901). *'Twixt Sirdar and Menelik.* London: Harper & Bros.

Willoughby, J. C. (1889). *East Africa and its Big Game.* London: Longmans Green.

Wollaston, A. F. R. (1908). *From Ruwenzori to the Congo.* London: John Murray.

Zeuner, F. E. (1963). *A History of Domesticated Animals.* London: Hutchinson.

Note: Since this book was written, the following important publication has appeared. Sidney, J. (1965). *The past and present distribution of some African ungulates. Trans. Zool. Soc. Lond.* **30**, 1-430.

INDEX